MONDAY Patterning and Algebra

1. Find x.

   $x + 23 = 55$

2. Write the expression in words.

   $5 + m$

3. What is the pattern rule?

   9, 14, 19, 24, 29

4. What will be the 10th term of this pattern?

   500, 460, 420, 380

5. Evaluate the expression where $x = 4$ and $y = 20$.

   $5x + 2y =$

TUESDAY Number Sense

1. Find the value.

   $2 \times 10^3 + 3 \times 10^2 + 1 \times 10^0 =$

2. Solve.

   20% of 320

3. Find the product:

   160×0.1

4. Write this number in words.

   689 427

5. Find the sum. Reduce your answer to lowest terms.

   $\frac{4}{8} + \frac{2}{16}$

WEDNESDAY Geometry

1. How many edges?

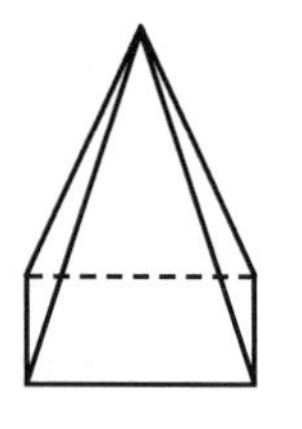

2. Classify the angle as *acute, obtuse*, *straight* or *right.*

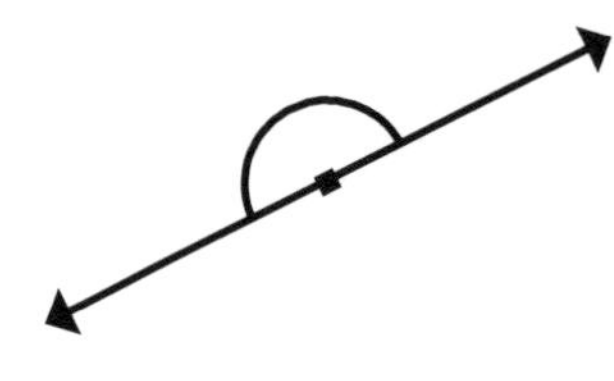

3. Name a quadrilateral.

4. Draw a pair of congruent shapes.

5. How many lines of symmetry?

THURSDAY Measurement

1. What is the area of a triangle width 15 m and heigh 10 m?

2. Find the circumference of a circle.

   diameter = 16 m

3. Solve in mm.

   6 m – 3 mm =

4. How many seconds in 6 hrs 20 mins?

5. What would be the best unit of measure to measure a glass of juice?

FRIDAY Data Management

Here are this week's standings in soccer for the local high school teams.

Team	Points Scored
Panthers	78
Pumas	72
Tigers	79
Broncos	60
Lions	24
Mustangs	60
Stingrays	36

Use the information in the table to answer the following questions.

1. What is the range of the data? ______________________

2. What team is leading in points scored? ______________________

3. What is the mean of the data? ______________________

4. What is the mode? ______________________

5. What is the best kind of graph to display this data? ______________________

BRAIN STRETCH

Ben purchased 12 boxes of candy at the local convenience store. Each box contained 15 pieces of candy. The boxes were $5.10 each. How much was a single piece of candy?

MONDAY Patterning and Algebra

1. What will be the 12th term of this pattern?

   7000, 700, 70, 7, 0.7

2. Find t.

   $6 \times 9 = t + 22$

3. What is the pattern rule?

   11, 16, 21, 26, 31

4. Write the expression in words.

   $3n - 2$

5. Evaluate the expression where $x = 40$ and $y = 9$.

   $5x - 2y =$

TUESDAY Number Sense

1. Find the value.

   $7 \times 10^3 + 2 \times 10^2 + 5 \times 10^0 =$

2. Write the percent as a fraction in simplest form.

   72%

3. Find the product:

   480×0.1

4. Find the unit rate. Round your answer to the nearest hundredth.

   117 roses in 9 rows

   ___________ in each row

5. Find the sum. Reduce your answer to lowest terms.

   $\frac{5}{8} + \frac{4}{16}$

WEDNESDAY Geometry

1. Name the part of the circle.

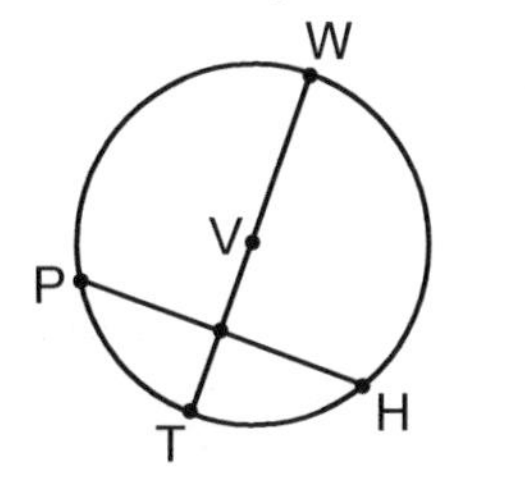

$\overline{WT}$

2. Define the term acute angle.

3. Classify the triangle as isosceles, scalene, or equilateral.

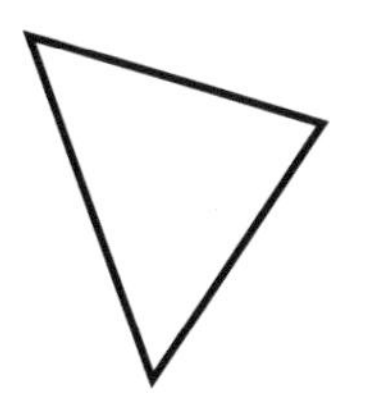

4. What is the measure of the missing angle?

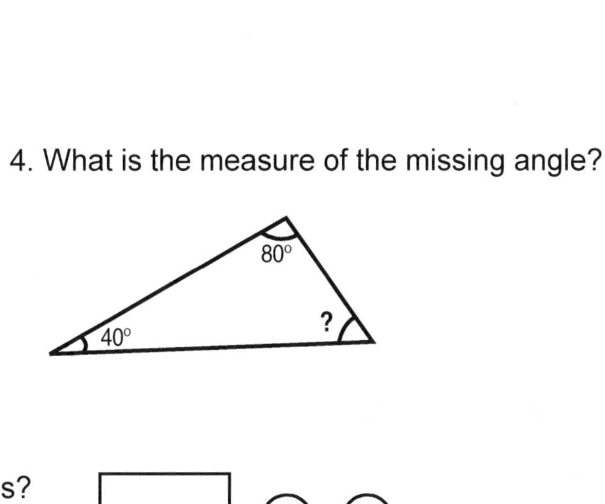

5. What 3D figure can you make from these pieces?

THURSDAY Measurement

1. What is the height of a triangle with base 16 cm and area 120 cm^2?

2. What is the elapsed time?

four in the afternoon to nine at night

3. Find the circumference.

radius = 17.11 m

4. 0.7839 g = ________ mg

5. Calculate the area of the parallelogram.

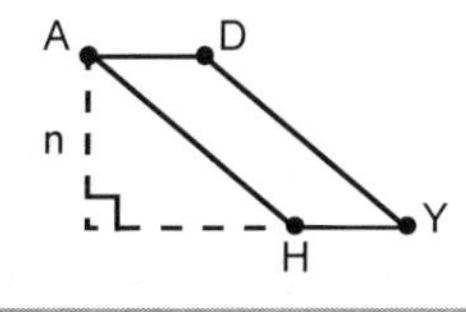

$\overline{AH}$ = 8.7 m $\overline{AD}$ = 3.3 m n = 4.5 m

FRIDAY Data Management

Find the mean, median, and mode of each set of data. Show your work.

1. 9, 13, 27, 3 and 3

2. 8, 3, 10, 22 and 22

3. 11, 25, 7, 15, 17, 16 and 7

4. 16, 11, 13, 15, 14, 14 and 15

BRAIN STRETCH

Megan worked as a salesperson and earned a 5% commission on a sale. If she sold a pair of shoes for $53.78, how much was her commission on the sale?

MONDAY Patterning and Algebra

1. Complete the function table.

Rule: $n = z + 5$

Input	Z	6	12	18	24
Output	N				

2. Find t.

$152 = 8t$

3. What is the pattern rule?

9, 15, 21, 27, 33

4. What will be the 7th term of this pattern?

$1, 1\frac{1}{2}, 2, 2\frac{1}{2}$

5. Evaluate the expression where $x = 5$ and $y = 16$.

$5x + 2y =$

TUESDAY Number Sense

1. Find the value.

56.09 + 3.2 – 4.1

2. What is the place value of the number in **bold**?

721 **4**95

3. Find the product:

150 x 0.3

4. Find the unit rate. Round your answer to the nearest hundredth.

$31.50 for 5 hours

_________ per hour

5. Solve.

$89\overline{)17\,088}$

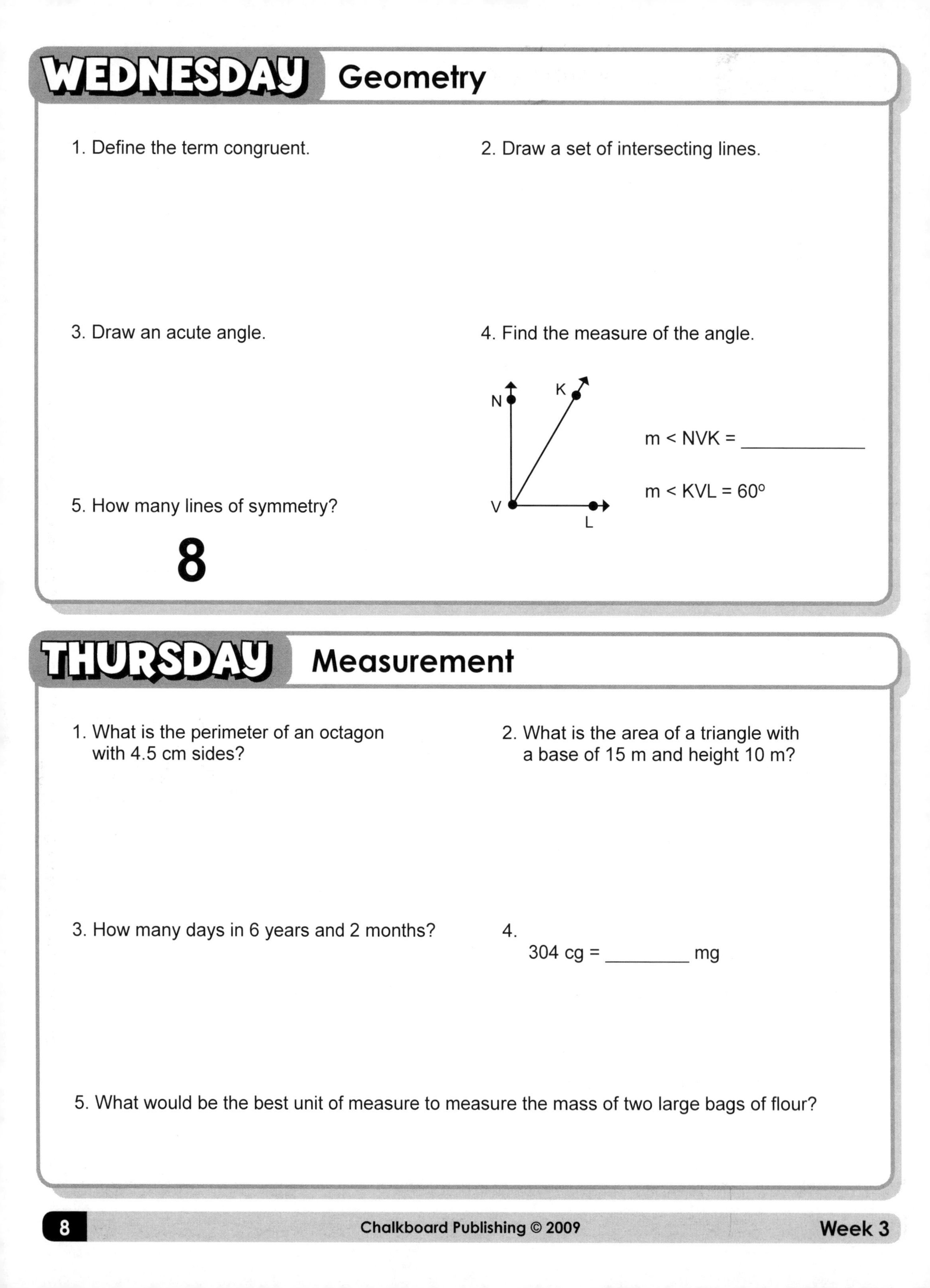

WEDNESDAY Geometry

1. Define the term congruent.

2. Draw a set of intersecting lines.

3. Draw an acute angle.

4. Find the measure of the angle.

m < NVK = ___________

m < KVL = 60°

5. How many lines of symmetry?

8

THURSDAY Measurement

1. What is the perimeter of an octagon with 4.5 cm sides?

2. What is the area of a triangle with a base of 15 m and height 10 m?

3. How many days in 6 years and 2 months?

4. 304 cg = ________ mg

5. What would be the best unit of measure to measure the mass of two large bags of flour?

FRIDAY Data Management

1. Sort factors into the Venn Diagram, using the rules listed below.

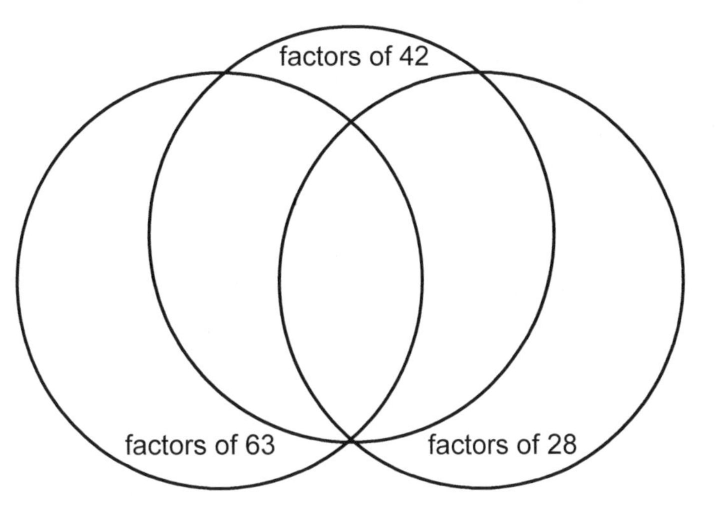

2. What is the greatest common factor? ______________________

3. What is the least common factor? ______________________

BRAIN STRETCH

Madelyn spent 4 hours at swim practice each week.

1. How many hours a year does she practice swimming?

2. How many hours will she have practised in 4 years?

3. How many minutes will she have practiced in 3 years?

MONDAY Patterning and Algebra

1. Complete the function table.

   Rule: f = h + 7

Input	h	37	39	41	43
Output	f				

2. Solve the equation.

   $240 \div b = 16$

3. Complete by evaluating the expression.

   $b^2 - 3b + 14$ for $b = 7$

4. What number comes next?

   3, 9, 27, 81, 243, ________

5. Write an expression for the phrase.

   ½ the length of a table decreased by 4 cm

TUESDAY Number Sense

1. Write the improper fraction as a mixed number in simplest form.

   $\frac{30}{9}$

2. Find the greatest common factor for this set of numbers.

   70 and 45

3. Find the unit rate. Round your answer to the nearest hundredth.

   315 candies in 9 bags

   _________ per bag

4. Add. Write the answer in simplest form.

   $4 + 19\frac{6}{13}$

5. Evaluate.

   42 + (-13 -21 -15)

WEDNESDAY Geometry

1. Draw an irregular quadrilateral.

2. What 3D figure does this object resemble?

3. Draw a pair of similar shapes.

4. What is an isosceles triangle?

5. Name a pair of right angles.

P L Y M J G

THURSDAY Measurement

1. Solve in kg.

   9 kg + 2 mg =

2. What is the height of a triangle with base 7 cm and area 87.5 cm^2?

3.
   15 m^2 = _________ cm^2

4. What is the elapsed time?

   twelve minutes after four in the morning to 6:56 in the morning

5. What would be the best unit of measure to measure the distance between two cities?

FRIDAY Data Management

1. Answer the probability questions using the information on the two spinners.

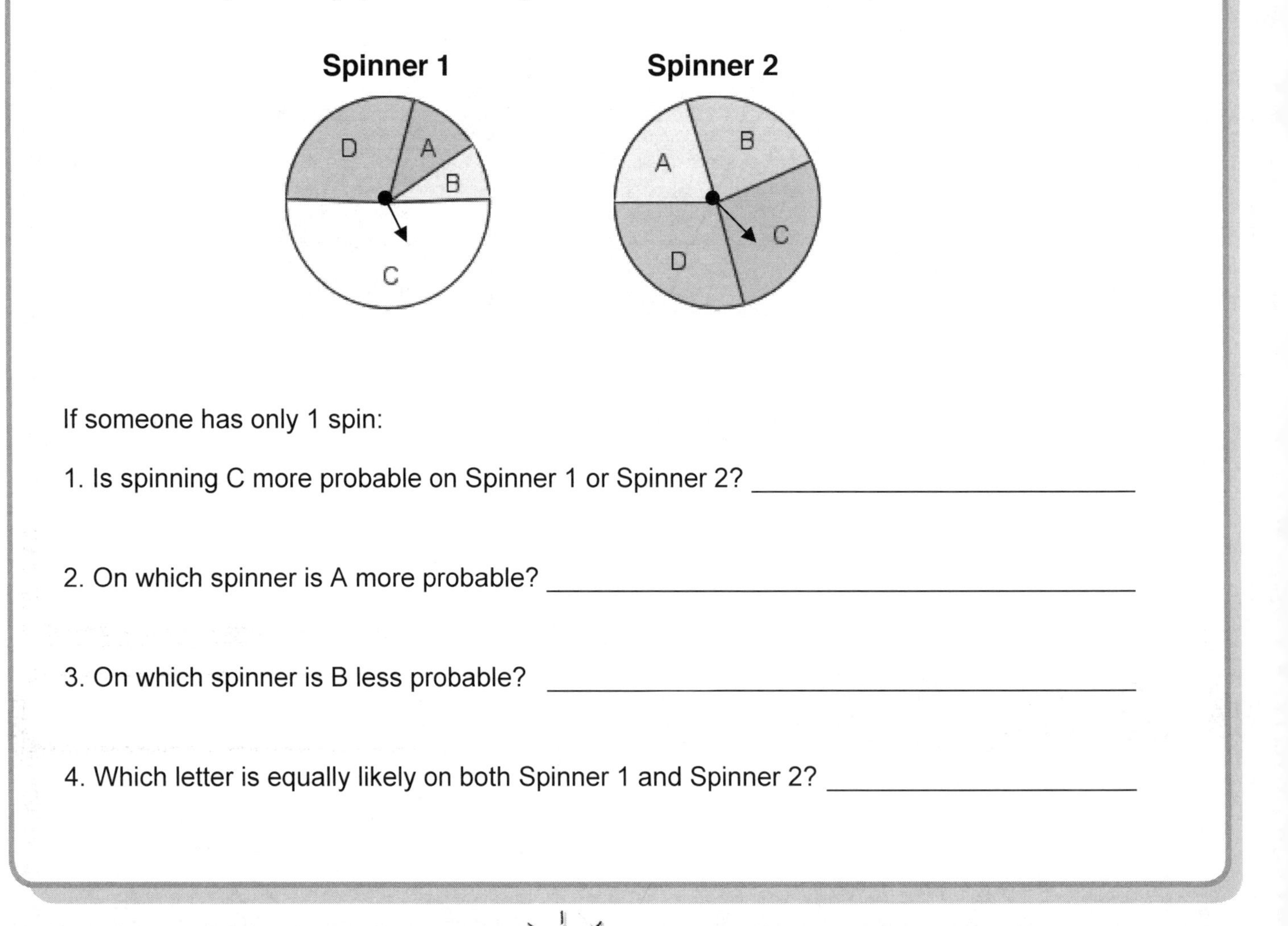

If someone has only 1 spin:

1. Is spinning C more probable on Spinner 1 or Spinner 2? ____________________

2. On which spinner is A more probable? ____________________

3. On which spinner is B less probable? ____________________

4. Which letter is equally likely on both Spinner 1 and Spinner 2? ____________________

BRAIN STRETCH

Mathew has five times as many CDs as Chris. Chris has one quarter as many CDs as Stephen. Stephen has 36 CDs. How many CDs does Mathew have?

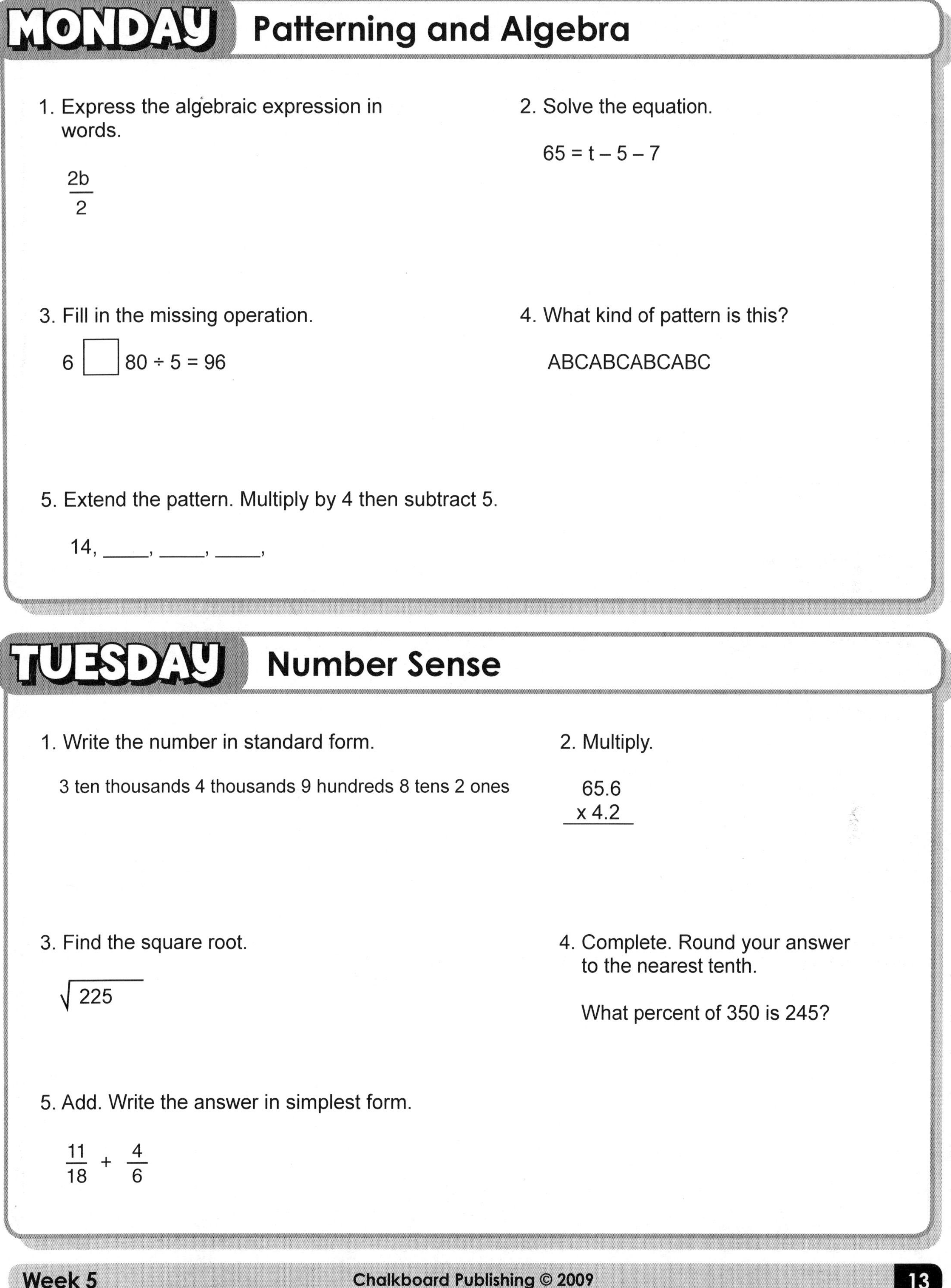

MONDAY Patterning and Algebra

1. Express the algebraic expression in words.

$$\frac{2b}{2}$$

2. Solve the equation.

$65 = t - 5 - 7$

3. Fill in the missing operation.

$6 \square 80 \div 5 = 96$

4. What kind of pattern is this?

ABCABCABCABC

5. Extend the pattern. Multiply by 4 then subtract 5.

14, ____, ____, ____,

TUESDAY Number Sense

1. Write the number in standard form.

3 ten thousands 4 thousands 9 hundreds 8 tens 2 ones

2. Multiply.

$$\begin{array}{r} 65.6 \\ \times\ 4.2 \\ \hline \end{array}$$

3. Find the square root.

$\sqrt{225}$

4. Complete. Round your answer to the nearest tenth.

What percent of 350 is 245?

5. Add. Write the answer in simplest form.

$$\frac{11}{18} + \frac{4}{6}$$

WEDNESDAY Geometry

1. Define the term similar figures.

2. Classify the angle as *acute, obtuse*, *straight* or *right.*

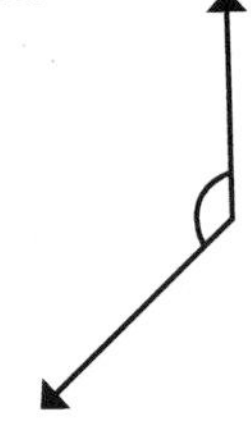

3. Draw a parallelogram.

4. How many faces?

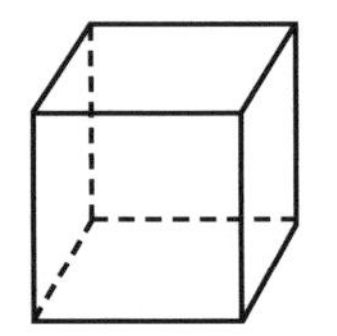

5. How many lines of symmetry?

THURSDAY Measurement

1. What is the length of the base of a triangle with height 22.2 mm and area 293.04 mm^2?

2. Find the circumference.

   radius = 7.71 mm

3. How many days in 5 months and 3 weeks?

4. 0.00877 g = ________ cg

5. Which is heavier? A kg of tissue or a kg of sugar?

FRIDAY Data Management

Clara Brenton Public School sold magazine subscriptions to raise money for school trips. Complete a bar graph to show the number of subscriptions sold by each grade.

Data Table

Grade	Number of Magazines
Class A	34
Class B	34
Class C	70
Class D	62
Class E	44
Class F	22

Answer the questions:

1. What was the range of number of magazines sold? ______________________

2. Which grade sold the most magazines? ______________________

3. Which class sold the least magazines? ______________________

4. What was the ratio of magazines sold by Class B to Class E? ______________

5. What was the median of magazines sold? ______________________

BRAIN STRETCH

A 600 seat stadium is divided into 3 sections. There are 210 seats in section 1, and there are 70 more seats in section 2 than in section 3. How many seats are in sections 2?

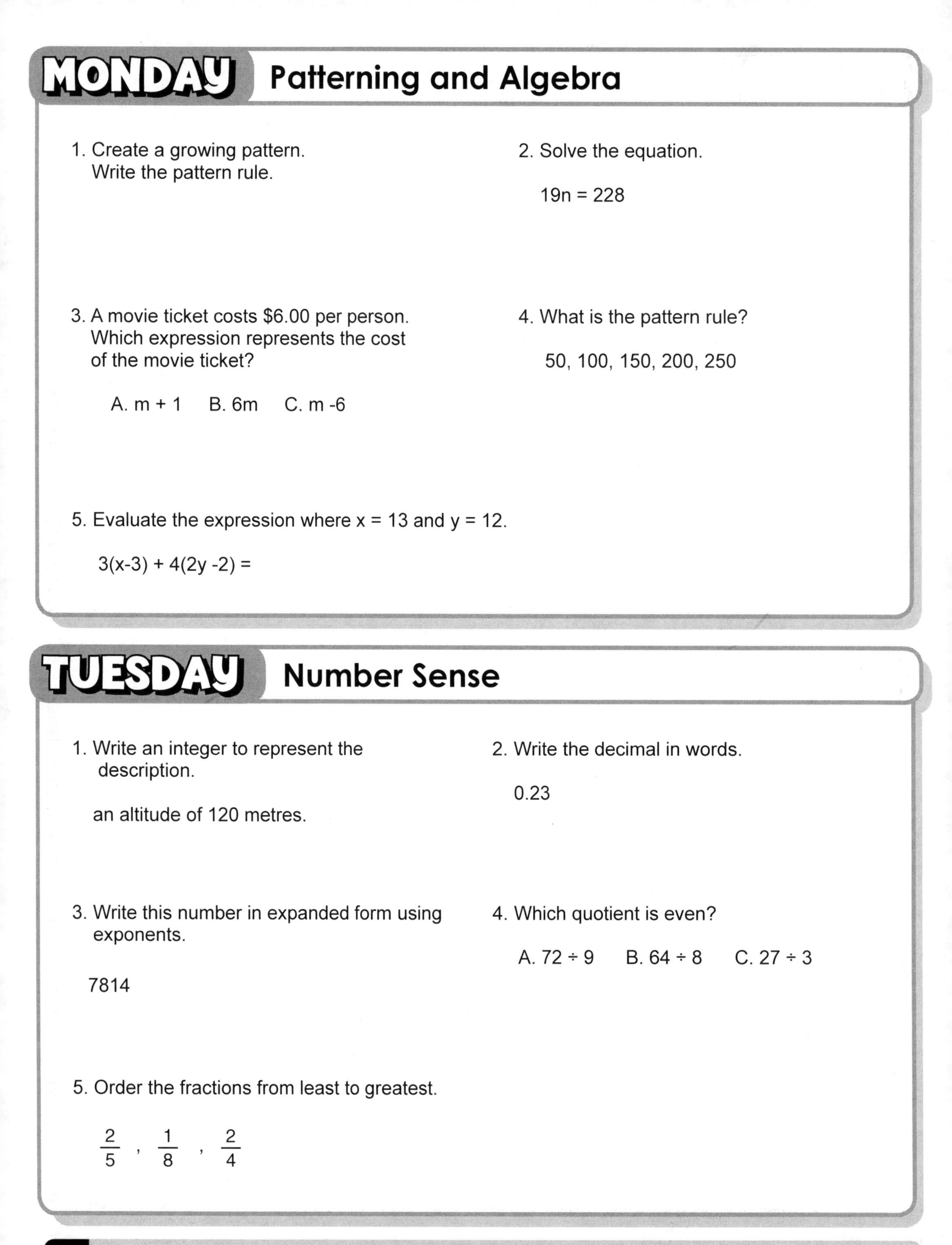

MONDAY Patterning and Algebra

1. Create a growing pattern. Write the pattern rule.

2. Solve the equation.

   $19n = 228$

3. A movie ticket costs $6.00 per person. Which expression represents the cost of the movie ticket?

   A. $m + 1$ B. $6m$ C. $m - 6$

4. What is the pattern rule?

   50, 100, 150, 200, 250

5. Evaluate the expression where $x = 13$ and $y = 12$.

   $3(x-3) + 4(2y-2) =$

TUESDAY Number Sense

1. Write an integer to represent the description.

   an altitude of 120 metres.

2. Write the decimal in words.

   0.23

3. Write this number in expanded form using exponents.

   7814

4. Which quotient is even?

   A. $72 \div 9$ B. $64 \div 8$ C. $27 \div 3$

5. Order the fractions from least to greatest.

   $\frac{2}{5}$, $\frac{1}{8}$, $\frac{2}{4}$

WEDNESDAY Geometry

1. How many vertices does a cube have?

2. What 3D figure can you make from these pieces?

3. What is an equilateral triangle?

4. What is the measure of the missing angle?

?

50°

5. Classify the triangle as isosceles, scalene, or equilateral and as right, acute, or obtuse.

THURSDAY Measurement

1. What is the area of a triangle with base 7 cm and height 17 cm?

2. Solve in cm.

   54 m + 20 cm =

3. What time is 21:30 on a 12 hour clock?

4. What is the elapsed time?

   8:16 a.m. to fifty-five minutes after twelve in the afternoon

5. Use the information to find the missing measure of the trapezoid.

height = 22 cm
b_1 = 7 cm
b_2 = ________
area = 341 cm^2

FRIDAY Data Management

Here is a double bar graph of the amount of money two classes collected for a class trip.

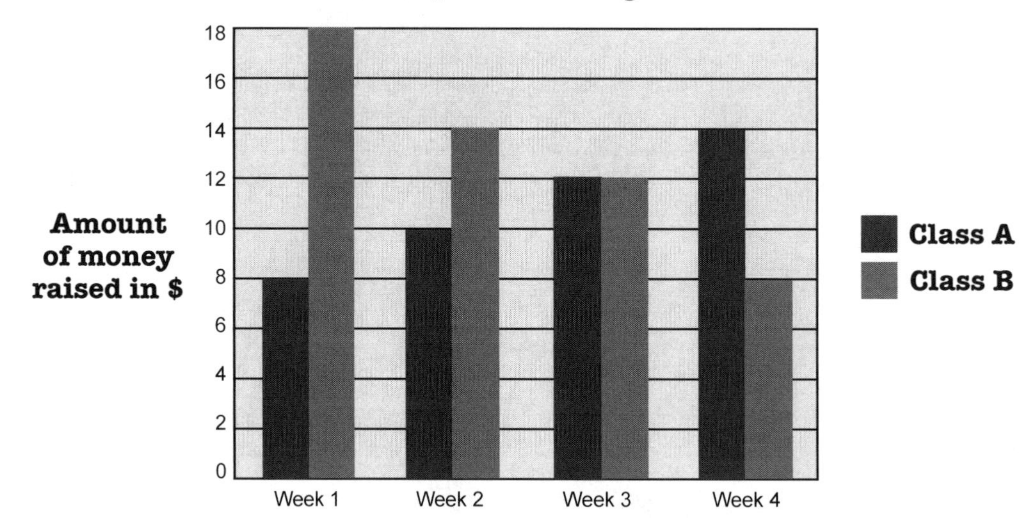

Use the information in the graph to write 2 statements about the data.

1. ______________________________

2. ______________________________

3. What would be a reasonable prediction about the amount of money raised for each class in week 5? Explain.

____

____

BRAIN STRETCH

A box of cookies weighs 360 grams. If Bessie brought two boxes for the class party, what is the combined weight of both boxes of cookies in kilograms?

MONDAY Patterning and Algebra

1. Express the phrase as an algebraic expression.

   the difference of 56 and a number is 61

2. Create a repeating pattern. Write the pattern rule.

3. Find the next number in the sequence.

   21, 63, 189, 567, _____

4. Find t.

   6 x 9 = t + 22

5. Complete the function table. Rule: t = p ÷9

Input	p	27	36	45	54
Output	t				

TUESDAY Number Sense

1. Subtract.

   $4351.62
   \- 117.04

2. Complete.

   41 + 42 × 32 + 105 ÷ 7

3. Rewrite the number in scientific notation.

   600 000

4. Subtract.

   24.57 - 4.48

5. Add. Write the answer in simplest form.

   $\frac{3}{7} + \frac{1}{5}$

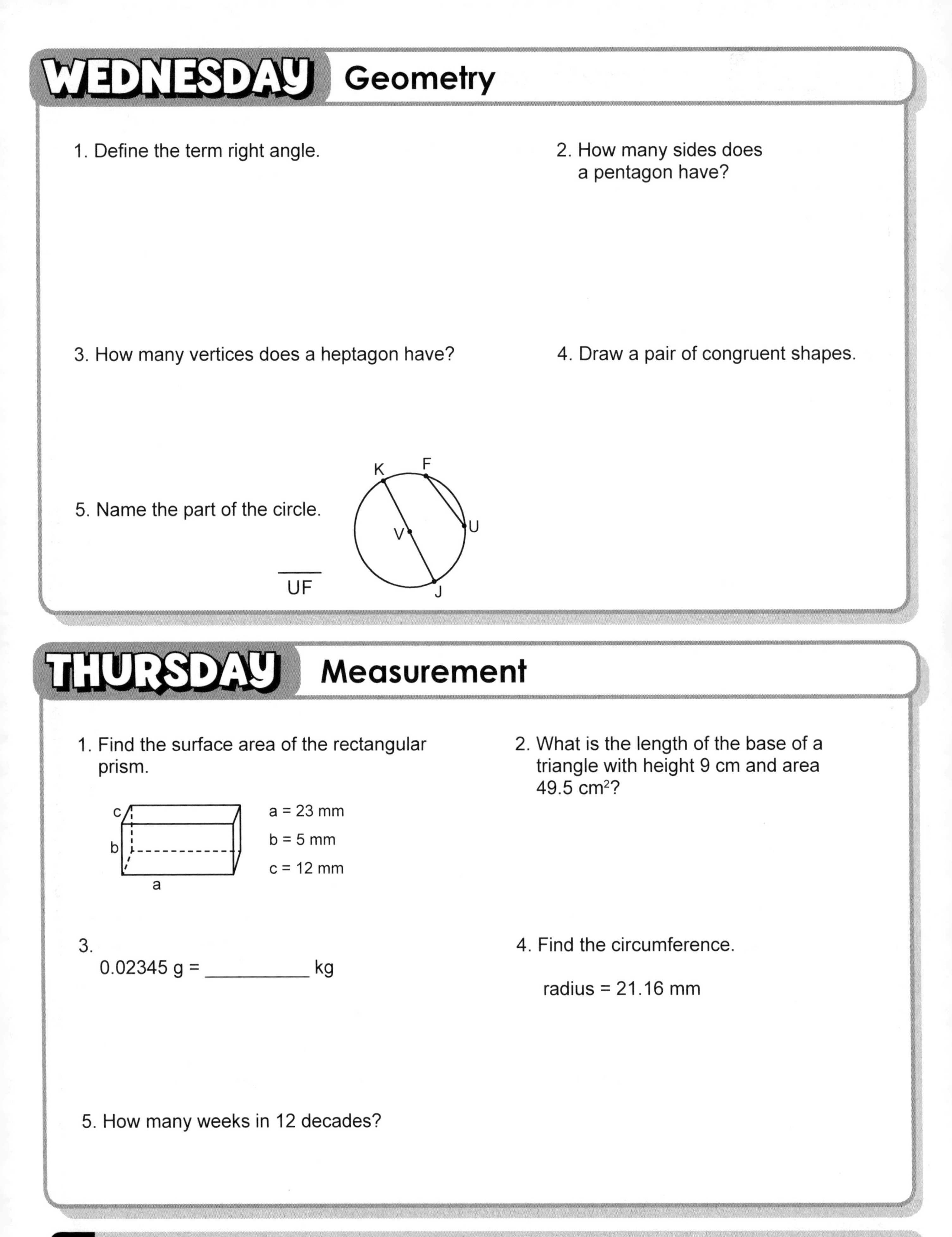

WEDNESDAY Geometry

1. Define the term right angle.

2. How many sides does a pentagon have?

3. How many vertices does a heptagon have?

4. Draw a pair of congruent shapes.

5. Name the part of the circle.

$\overline{UF}$

THURSDAY Measurement

1. Find the surface area of the rectangular prism.

a = 23 mm

b = 5 mm

c = 12 mm

2. What is the length of the base of a triangle with height 9 cm and area 49.5 cm^2?

3. 0.02345 g = __________ kg

4. Find the circumference.

radius = 21.16 mm

5. How many weeks in 12 decades?

FRIDAY Data Management

Do you think the following graphs are misleading? Explain your thinking.

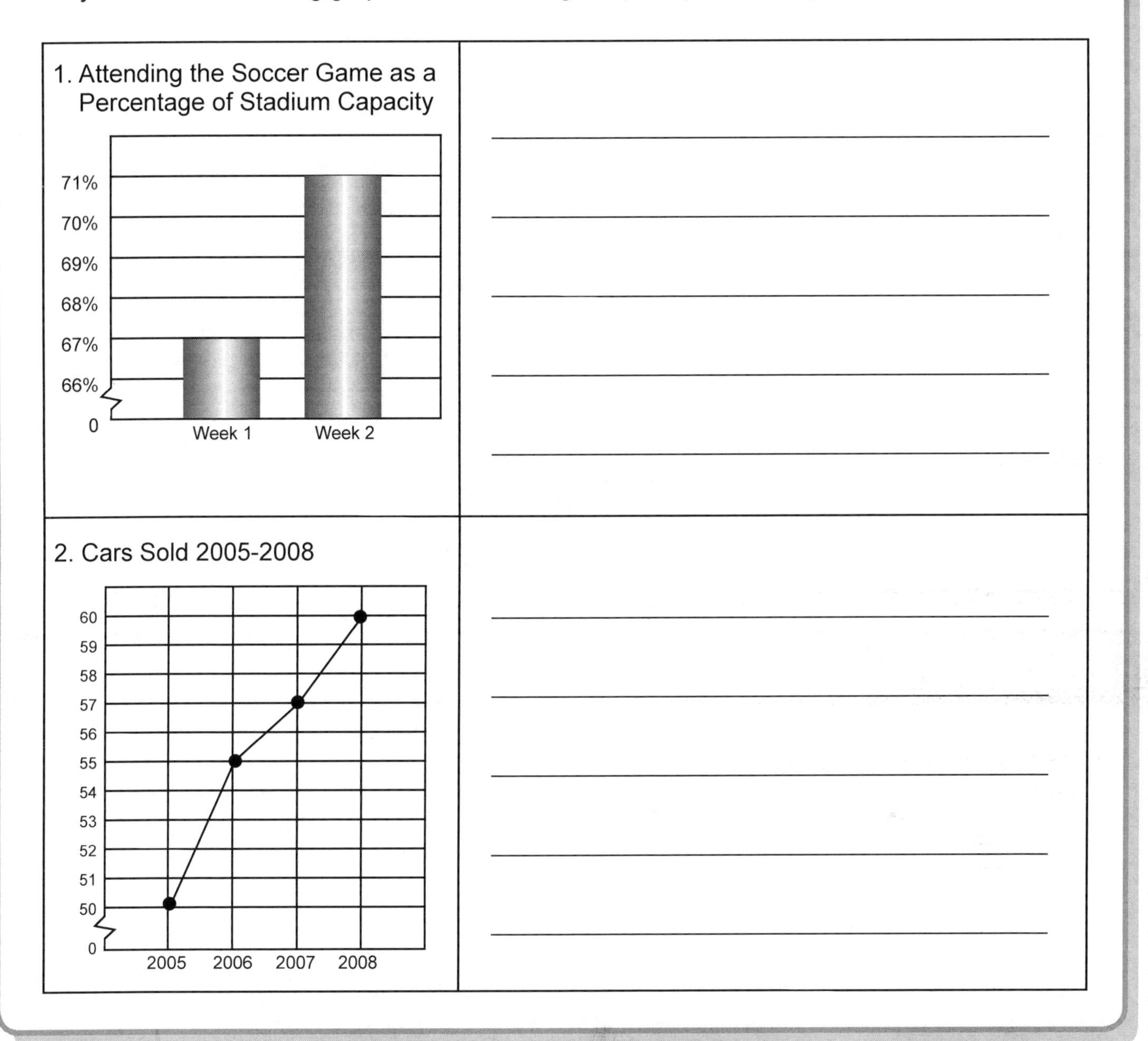

BRAIN STRETCH

The total rainfall for two days was 14.6 mm. The first day's total was 4.5 mm less than the second day's. How much rain fell on each day in cm?

MONDAY Patterning and Algebra

1. Solve the inequality.

   If $8X + 2 > 34$ Then $X >$ ______

2. Solve the equation.

   $165 = 11h$

3. Express the phrase as an algebraic expression.

   47 decreased by a number p

4. What will be the 7th term of this pattern?

   2, 22, 222, 2222,

5. Evaluate the expression where $a = 6$, and $b = 2$.

   $9a(b-1)$

TUESDAY Number Sense

1. Write the number in expanded form using exponents.

   3334

2. Add.

   $31.25 + 23.47$

3. Write the number in standard form.

   nine million five hundred sixty-one thousand six hundred five

4. Multiply.

$$\begin{array}{r} 236.7 \\ \times\ 0.34 \\ \hline \end{array}$$

5. Order the fractions from greatest to least.

   $\frac{1}{2}, \frac{3}{9}, \frac{5}{14}$

WEDNESDAY Geometry

1. Define the term right triangle.

2. Classify the angle as *acute, obtuse*, *straight* or *right.*

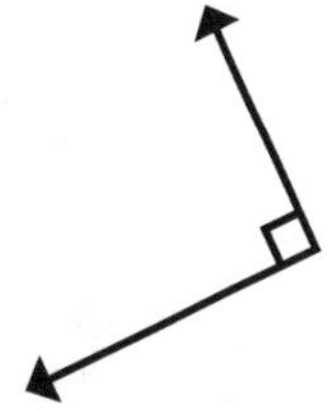

3. Classify the triangle as *isosceles, scalene,* or *equilateral* and as *right, acute*, or *obtuse*.

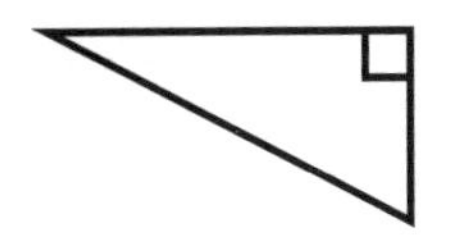

4. How many vertices does a hexagon have?

5. Name a pair of complementary angles.

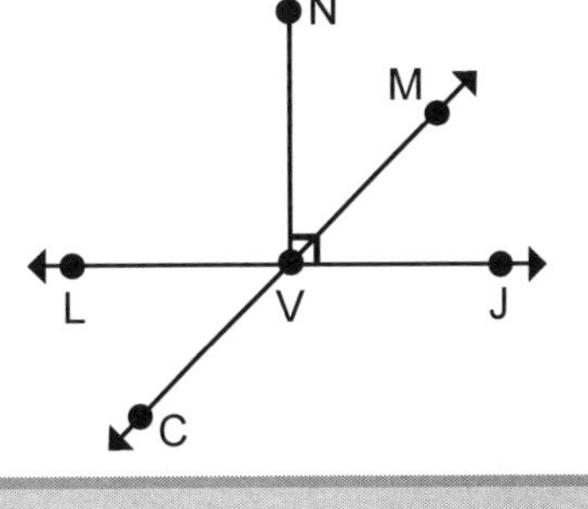

THURSDAY Measurement

1. What is the area of a triangle with base 6.1 cm and height 7.8 cm?

2. What is the elapsed time?

   5:53 a.m. to 5:20 p.m.

3. Solve in cL.

   12 L - 3 cL =

4. What would be the best unit of measure to measure the height of a school?

5. Calculate the area of the parallelogram.

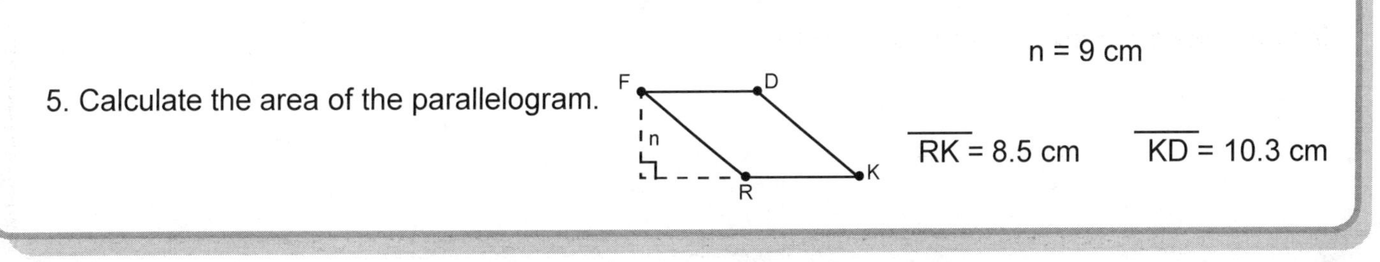

FRIDAY Data Management

Here is a circle graph that shows how middle school students travel to school. Use the information to answer the questions.

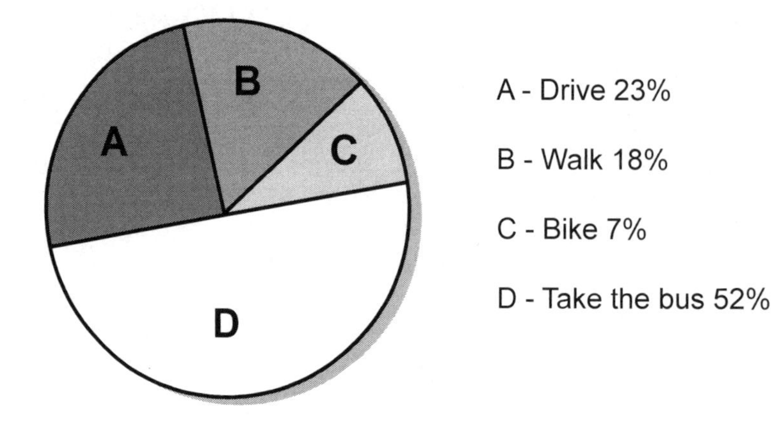

1. If there are 120 students, how many students walk to school? ____________

2. What fraction of the students drive to school? ____________

3. What fraction of the students take the bus? ____________

4. What percentage of students either walks or drives to school? ____________

5. What is the most popular way to get to school? ____________

BRAIN STRETCH

Katherine and her mother went into a grocery store to buy 4 dozen eggs. When they opened the egg cartons at home they saw that 2/3 of the eggs were broken. What fractional part of the eggs were not broken?

MONDAY Patterning and Algebra

1. Solve the inequality.

   If $3X + 7 < 13$ Then $X <$ _____

2. Solve the equation.

   $6 = 30 \div n$

3. Find the next number in the sequence.

   25, 75, 225, 675, _____

4. Extend the pattern.
   Multiply by -6 then subtract 3.

   9, ____, ____, ____,

5. Complete the function table. Rule: $w = x-10$

Input	x	29	37	38	51
Output	w				

TUESDAY Number Sense

1. List all of the factors for the number:

   35

2. Order from least to greatest.

   0.3375, 0.3625, ¼

3. Fill in the missing number.

   $\frac{\_\_}{98} = \frac{3}{7}$

4. Which quotient is odd?

   A. $60 \div 2$ B. $10 \div 5$ C. $121 \div 11$

5. Add. Write the answer in simplest form.

   $\frac{2}{3} + \frac{7}{8}$

WEDNESDAY Geometry

1. Draw an obtuse angle.

2. Find the measure of the angle.

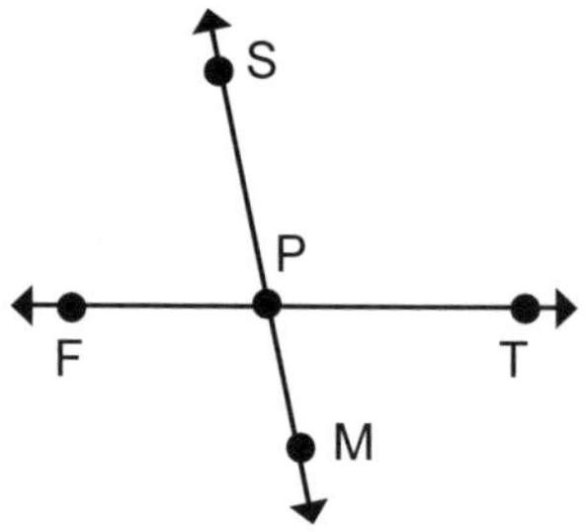

m < TPS = ____________

m < FPM = 96°

3. Define the term straight angle.

4. How many sides does a quadrilateral have?

5. Name the part of the circle.

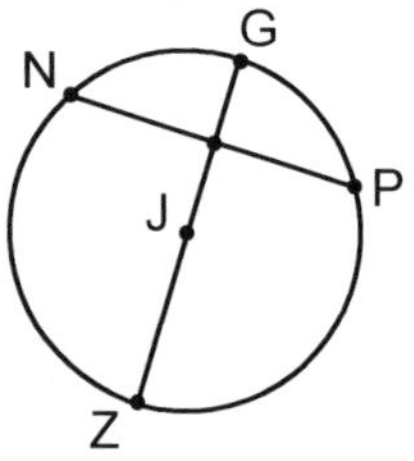

$\overline{JZ}$

THURSDAY Measurement

1. What time is 14:20 on a 12 hour clock?

2. Solve in cL.

12 kL + 5 cL =

3. What would the temperature be on a cold day?

-3°C, 10°C or 23°C

4. How many days in 4 centuries?

5. What are the dimensions of a square with a area of 36 m^2?

FRIDAY Data Management

How do people use data management in everyday life? Explain your thinking.

BRAIN STRETCH

Spencer and Ben each received $12.50 for an allowance each week. Spencer spent 1/5 of his money on going to the movies. Ben spent 10% of his money on candy. How much money do they have left over together?

MONDAY Patterning and Algebra

1. Extend the pattern.
   Multiply by -3 then add 5.

   4, ____, ____, ____,

2. Create a repeating pattern.

3. Show the first three numbers of this pattern:

   start at 6, multiply by 5

   ____, ____, ____

4. Solve the equation.

   $6 = 3p$

5. Evaluate the expression where $a = 9$, and $b = 4$.

   $a^2 + 3b$

TUESDAY Number Sense

1. Write the numeral 1 495 321 in expanded form.

2. Multiply.

   $$\begin{array}{r} 14.5 \\ \times\ 0.85 \\ \hline \end{array}$$

3. List all of the factors for the number:

   78

4. Complete

   $98 \div (5 + 9) + 19 \times 47 - 3$

5. Order the fractions from greatest to least.

   $\frac{2}{3}$, $\frac{1}{4}$, $\frac{5}{8}$

WEDNESDAY Geometry

1. How many edges?

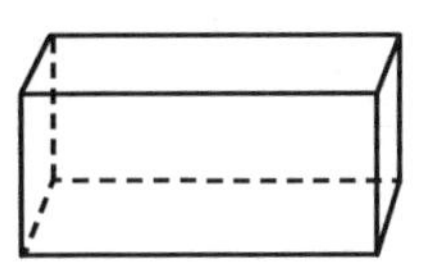

2. What is the measure of the missing angle?

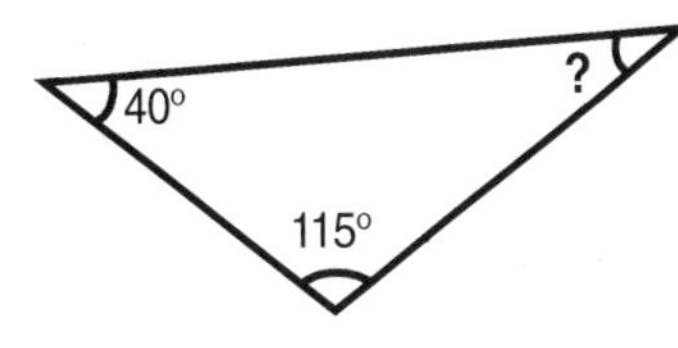

3. Name a shape with two sets of parallel sides.

4. Draw a pair of similar shapes.

5. Classify the triangle as isosceles, scalene, or equilateral.

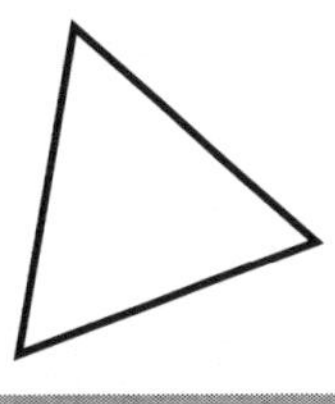

THURSDAY Measurement

1. What is the area of a triangle with base 29 cm and height 29 cm?

2. Find the circumference.

   diameter = 38 cm

3.
   0.009 cg = ____ mg

4. What is the volume of a cube that has 5 m sides?

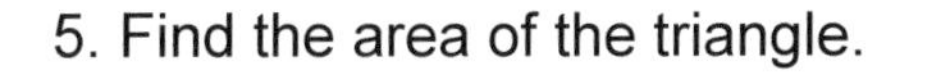

5. Find the area of the triangle.

$\overline{ZC}$ = 80 m $\overline{ZV}$ = 98 m $\overline{CV}$ = 73 m

n = 72 m

FRIDAY Data Management

Match the math term with its definition.

A. probability	B. mean	C. data	D. graph	E. bar graph
F. median	G. range	H. pictograph	I. mode	J. circle graph

1. _______ found by dividing the sum of the numbers by the number of numbers in the set.

2. _______ the middle number in a set of numbers arranged in order.

3. _______ the value that occurs most often in a set of data.

4. _______ a visual representation of data.

5. _______ a graph in which a circle is used to display data.

6. _______ a graph that used pictures to display data.

7. _______ facts or information.

8. _______ a number from zero to one that shows how likely it is that an event will happen.

9. _______ a graph made up of horizontal or vertical bars.

10. ______ the difference between the smallest value and the greatest value in set of data.

BRAIN STRETCH

A case of soda pop has 24 cans or 4 six-packs. One case of soda pop costs $8.44.
A six pack of soda pop costs $2.24. Which is the better buy? Explain.

MONDAY Patterning and Algebra

1. Express the following problem algebraically.

   a number increased by 2 is 37

2. Solve the equation.

   $27 \div g = 3$

3. Find the missing number in the sequence.

   22, 44, _____, 176

4. Solve the inequality.

   If $4X + 10 < 22$ Then $X <$ ____

5. Complete the function table. Rule: $n = z^3$

Input	z	3	4	5	6
Output	n				

TUESDAY Number Sense

1. Multiply.

   235×8

2. Divide.

   $1220 \div 2$

3. Name a composite number.

4. Find the greatest common factor.

   54 and 18

5. Add. Write the answer in simplest form.

   $\frac{3}{10} + \frac{10}{15}$

WEDNESDAY Geometry

1. Name the part of the circle.

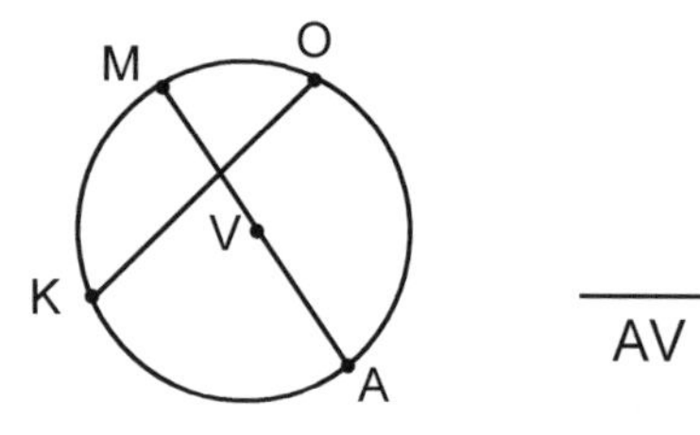

$\overline{AV}$

2. Draw a pair of congruent shapes.

3. Name a pair of vertical angles.

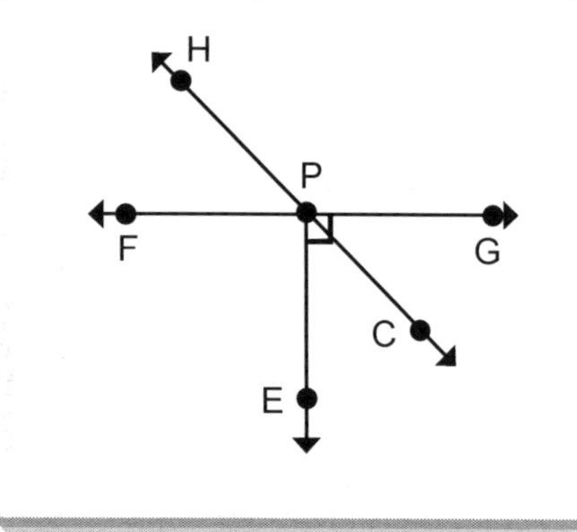

4. Draw a shape without any parallel sides.

5. Draw a pair of similar shapes.

THURSDAY Measurement

1. How many seconds in one day?

2.

595 000 m = ___ km

3. What would be the best unit of measure to measure the length of a centipede.

4. What is the elapsed time?

12:19 in the afternoon to 10:44 at night

5. Find the area of the triangle.

E

n

B C

$\overline{BE} = 80$ m $\quad \overline{BC} = 93$ m $\quad \overline{CE} = 108$ m $\quad n = 78$ m

FRIDAY Data Management

The students at Orchard Park Public School held a canned food drive. Here are the results of their efforts.

	Week 1	Week 2	Week 3
Monday	27	40	13
Tuesday	11	44	8
Wednesday	30	22	13
Thursday	18	33	27
Friday	14	15	8

1. What was the total number of food cans collected in week 1?

2. What was the mean of the number of canned food collected daily in Week 3?

3. How many food cans were collected on the past three Wednesdays?

4. What was the median number of canned food collected in week 2?

BRAIN STRETCH

John ran 100 metres in 51 seconds. Rob ran 1 kilometre in 4 minutes 12 seconds. Who was the fastest runner? Explain your thinking.

MONDAY Patterning and Algebra

1. Solve the equation. p=10

   (35 ÷ p + 2)

2. Create a repeating pattern.

3. Fill in the missing operation.

   83 × 1 - 46 ☐ 5 = 42

4. Find in the missing number in the sequence.

   _______, 81, 27, 9

5. Show the first three numbers of this pattern: start with 2.5 and add 8.5 each time

   _______, _______, _______

TUESDAY Number Sense

1. Rewrite the number in scientific notation.

   200 000

2. Find the least common multiple.

   2, 6, and 12

3. Order the numbers from least to greatest.

   7408; 7501; 7390; 7400

4. Which product is even?

   A. 30 X 2 B. 5 X 5 C. 9 X 7

5. Subtract. Write the answer in simplest form.

   $\frac{1}{\quad} - \frac{7}{16}$

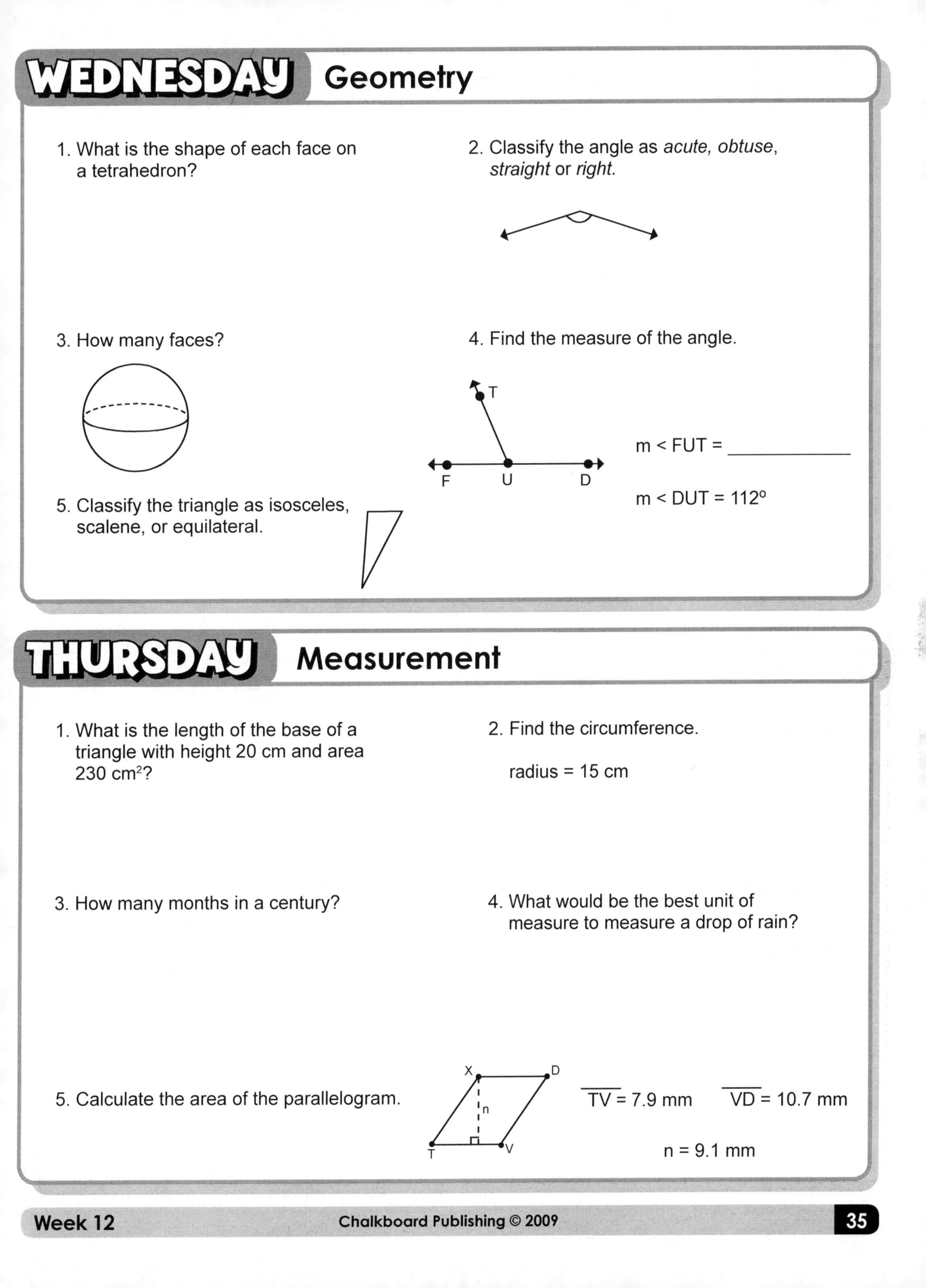

WEDNESDAY Geometry

1. What is the shape of each face on a tetrahedron?

2. Classify the angle as *acute, obtuse*, *straight* or *right.*

3. How many faces?

4. Find the measure of the angle.

m < FUT = ____________

m < DUT = 112°

5. Classify the triangle as isosceles, scalene, or equilateral.

THURSDAY Measurement

1. What is the length of the base of a triangle with height 20 cm and area 230 cm^2?

2. Find the circumference.

radius = 15 cm

3. How many months in a century?

4. What would be the best unit of measure to measure a drop of rain?

5. Calculate the area of the parallelogram.

$\overline{TV}$ = 7.9 mm $\overline{VD}$ = 10.7 mm

n = 9.1 mm

FRIDAY Data Management

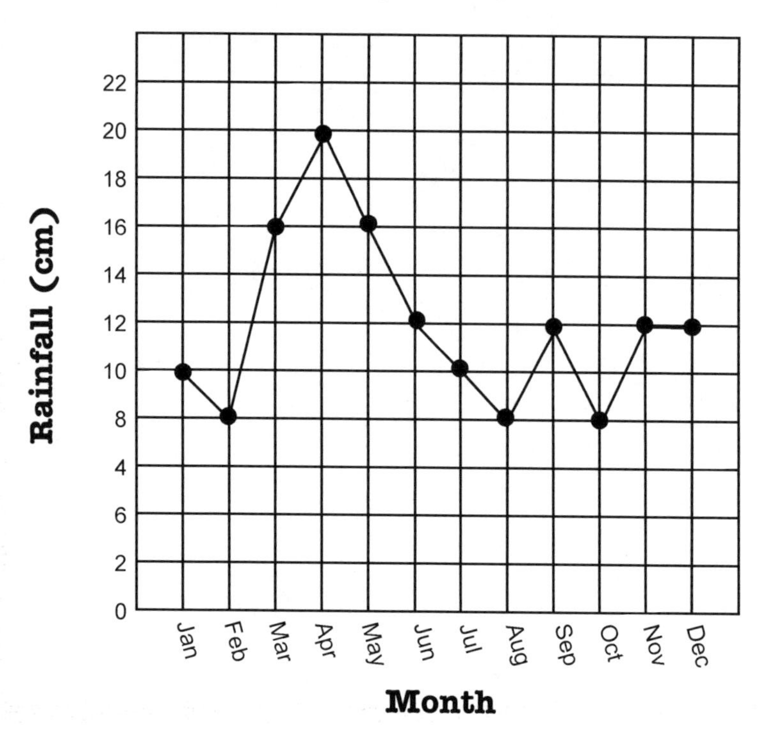

1. Between which two months was the greatest increase in precipitation?

____

2. Which month had the most precipitation?

____

3. What was the range of precipitation?

____

4. What was the mean of precipitation?

____

5. How much precipitation was there in August and October?

____

BRAIN STRETCH

If the temperature starts out in the morning at 12° C but drops 18° by midnight, what is the new temperature then?

MONDAY Patterning and Algebra

1. Find the missing number in the sequence.

   -11, -10, ______, -8

2. Write the expression in words.

   $5n + 9$

3. Express the phrase as an algebraic expression.

   difference of a number m and 5

4. Show the first three numbers of this pattern:

   start with 0.05 and add 2.5 each time

   _______, _______, _______

5. Evaluate the expression where a = 5, and b = 7.

   $b^3 \div 7 + a$

TUESDAY Number Sense

1. Find the square root.

   $\sqrt{121}$

2. Simplify.

   $66 \div 6 \times 1 + 47 + 5$

3. Find the least common multiple.

   50 and 100

4. What is the place value of the number in **bold**?

   2 1**7**0 093

5. Fill in the missing number.

   $\frac{48}{} = \frac{}{}$

WEDNESDAY Geometry

1. Name the shape.

2. Find the measure of the missing angle.

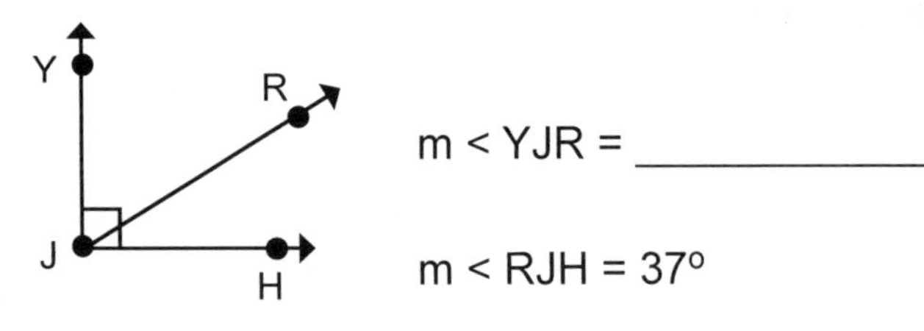

m < YJR = ____________

m < RJH = 37°

3. What 3D figure does this object look like?

4. How many lines of symmetry?

M

5. Name a pair of vertical angles.

THURSDAY Measurement

1. Solve in kg.

12 kg - 600 mg = _________

2. Find the circumference.

radius = 21.82 cm

3. 0.7 cm = _____ m

4. How many minutes in 22.5 hours?

5. Use the information to find the missing measure of the trapezoid.

height = _________

b_1 = 7 cm

b_2 = 6 cm

area = 56 cm^2

FRIDAY Data Management

Mrs. Stephenson kept a gardener's journal to track the growth of her geranium plants. Here is the data she collected in June and July.

Plant	June	July
#1	10 cm	14 cm
#2	9 cm	11 cm
#3	12 cm	13 cm
#4	12 cm	15 cm
#5	11 cm	12 cm
#6	14 cm	17 cm
#7	8 cm	11 cm

1. What is the range of the data in July?

2. What is the mean height to the nearest tenth, of the plants in June?

3. What is the mode in June?

4. Which plant had the greatest increase in height?

BRAIN STRETCH

Sophie baked some cookies. She wanted to serve them hot from the oven for dessert at 7:20 p.m. The cookies needed to bake for 32 minutes. What time did Sophie need to put the cookies into the oven?

MONDAY Patterning and Algebra

1. Create a growing pattern.
   Write the pattern rule.

2. Evaluate the expression.
   For $u = 3$

   $12u - u^2$

3. Which expression has the same value as h^3 ?

   A. $h \times h \times h$
   B. $3h$
   C. $h + 3$

4. Extend the pattern.
   Multiply by 11 then subtract 1.

   7, ______, ______, ______,

5. Complete the function table. Rule: $j = 5b$

Input	b	5	6	7	8
Output	j				

TUESDAY Number Sense

1. Multiply.

$$\begin{array}{r} 72 \\ \times\ 0.76 \\ \hline \end{array}$$

2. What is the place value of the number in **bold**?

   1**2**0 598

3. Write the fraction in simplest form.

   $\underline{48}$

4. Evaluate.

   24^2

5. Simplify.

   $18 \div 2 - (98 \div 2) + 48$

WEDNESDAY Geometry

How is geometry used in everyday life? Explain your thinking.

THURSDAY Measurement

1. What time is 2:00 p.m. on a 24 hour clock?

2. What is the area of a triangle with base 25.6 mm and height 12.3 mm?

3. 3.457 L = ___________ mL

4. Solve in km.

   12 km – 4 m =

5. How many minutes in 2 days and 12 hours?

FRIDAY Data Management

Complete a line graph using the data from the table to show hockey game attendance at Oakridge Public School.

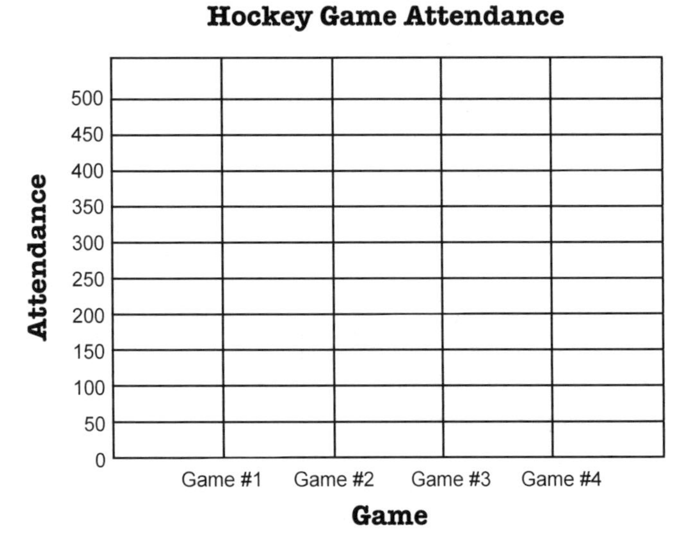

Game	# of People
Game #1	200
Game #2	350
Game #3	450
Game #4	100

Answer the following questions.

1. Which game(s) did not have an attendance of at least 350 people? ________________

2. What was the range of attendance? ________________

3. What was the average attendance? ________________

4. How many people altogether attended all four games? ________________

5. Which game showed an increase of 150 people from the week before? ________________

BRAIN STRETCH

At the grocery store, Coco Choco Bars outsells Cinamon Granola Bars by a five-to-one ratio. If the store sold 246 bars, how many of them were Cinnamon Granola Bars?

MONDAY Patterning and Algebra

1. $u^2 - 5u + 3$

   For $u = 7$

2. Create a shrinking pattern. Write the pattern rule.

3. Write an equation for the problem. Then solve the equation.

   the difference between 17 and a number is 6

4. Find the missing number in the sequence.

   _______, 27, 9, 3

5. Evaluate the expression where $a = 3$, and $b = 8$.

   $3(6 - a) + 4b$

TUESDAY Number Sense

1. List all of the factors for the number: 49

2. Calculate.

   9^3

3. Write the improper fraction as a mixed number in simplest form.

   $\frac{47}{10}$

4. Simplify.

   $(48 \div 6) + (1 \times 3 + 23)$

5. Subtract.

   $$\begin{array}{r} \$34\,941.20 \\ -\ 3\,072.76 \\ \hline \end{array}$$

WEDNESDAY Geometry

1. Define the term scalene triangle.

2. What 3D figure can you make from these pieces?

3. Draw and label a right triangle.

4. Find the measure of the angle.

K U S N

m < KUN = ___________

m < SUN = 81°

5. What is the name of this 3D figure?

THURSDAY Measurement

1. How many seconds 33 minutes?

2. 49 cm = ______ km

3. What time is 8:00 p.m. on a 24 hour clock?

4. What is the elapsed time?

9:32 in the morning to 4:42 in the afternoon

5. Dave went to the store to buy fencing for his backyard. His garden is twenty metres by seventeen metres and in the shape of a rectangle. How much fencing does he need to buy?

FRIDAY Data Management

Select the type of graph that would be best to display the data for the purpose stated.

Bar Graph   Double Bar Graph   Circle Graph   Line Graph   Pictograph   Scatter Plot

1. To determine the most popular type of music listened to by adults between the ages of 19 and 25.

____

2. To compare the time spent on different activities over a time period.

____

3. To understand the change of temperature over a period of time.

____

4. To look for a relationship between the number of hours students in a class studied for a test and the mark they received.

____

5. To compare the number of different types of movies seen by two classes during the month of May.

____

6. To compare the number of hours two different children practice piano every night for a week.

____

BRAIN STRETCH

David painted the wall in his bedroom. It took him 2 hours and 22 minutes and he was able to paint at a rate of 6 square m per hour. If the wall is eleven m long how tall is it?
Round your answer to the nearest metre.

MONDAY Patterning and Algebra

1. Evaluate the expression.
   for p = 7

   7p - 28

2. Create a repeating pattern.
   Write the pattern rule.

3. Solve the inequality.

   If 4X + 10 < 58   Then X < ____

4. Express the following problem algebraically.

   100 less than a number equals - 80

5. Show the first three numbers of this pattern: start with 72.8 and subtract 2.2 each time.

   ______, ______, ______

TUESDAY Number Sense

1. Round the number to the nearest ten thousands.

   56 322

2. Add.

   $$\begin{array}{r} \$\ 71\ 804.66 \\ +\ 22\ 091.83 \\ \hline \end{array}$$

3. List all of the factors for the number:

   91

4. Which product is odd?

   A. 18 X 4   B. 7 X 8   C. 11 X 3

5. Subtract. Write the answer in simplest form.

   $\frac{5}{7} - \frac{6}{11}$

WEDNESDAY Geometry

1. How many faces?

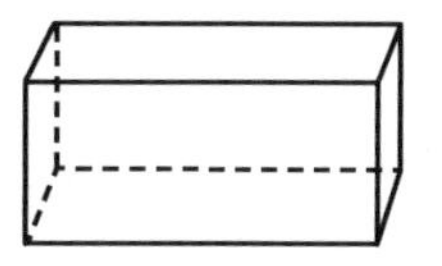

2. Draw a set of parallel lines.

3. Draw and label an isosceles triangle.

4. What 3D figure does this object resemble?

5. Name a pair of vertical angles.

L A Y S E Z

THURSDAY Measurement

1. What is the length of the base of a triangle with height 22 m and area 264 m^2?

2. Find the circumference.

diameter = 46 cm

3. 731 L = _______ cL

4. What would be the best unit of measure to measure the weight of an elephant?

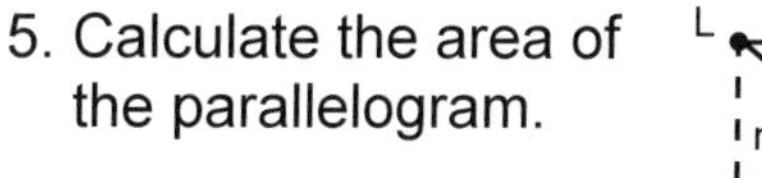

5. Calculate the area of the parallelogram.

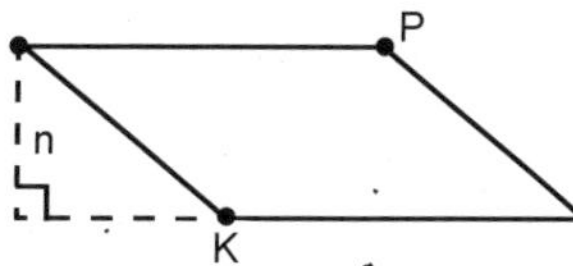

$\overline{KE} = 8.6$ cm $\overline{EP} = 5.3$ cm n = 4.1 cm

FRIDAY Data Management

Read the survey question. Then list a sample that you think would be more likey to be biased and a sample that you think would be less likely to be biased. Explain your thinking.

1. Survey Question: Are new cars too expensive?

Likely Biased Randomly Selected Sample: ______________________________

____

Likely Non-Biased Randomly Selected Sample ___________________________

____

2. Survey Question: Does the city need more children's playgrounds?

Likely Biased Randomly Selected Sample: ______________________________

____

Likely Non-Biased Randomly Selected Sample ___________________________

____

3. Survey Question: Should hospitals get more funding?

Likely Biased Randomly Selected Sample: ______________________________

____

Likely Non-Biased Randomly Selected Sample ___________________________

____

BRAIN STRETCH

If the perimeter of an equilateral triangle is 72 centimetres, what is the length of one of its sides in milimetres?

MONDAY Patterning and Algebra

1. Which expression is equivalent to 81, where a = 3?

   A. $3a^2$ B. $4a^3$ C. $3a^3$

2. There were 254 people who attended a hockey game. If each ticket cost $6.00 how much money was collected?

3. Find the missing number in the sequence.

   2560, 640, ________, 40

4. Evaluate the expression where a = 6 and b = 2.

   $2(b + 3) - 2a$

5. Complete the function table. Rule: $v = 30 \div k$

Input	k	30	15	5	6
Output	v				

TUESDAY Number Sense

1. What is 29% of 108?

2. Find the prime factorization for the number:

   22

3. How many eggs in 7 dozen?

4. Write the improper fraction as a mixed number in simplest form.

   $\frac{37}{16}$

5. Write the expression in exponential form and find the value.

   $3 \times 3 \times 3 \times 3 \times 3$

WEDNESDAY Geometry

1. How many edges?

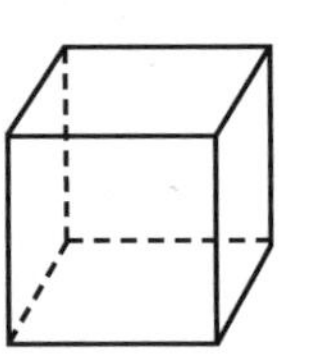

2. Classify the angle as acute, obtuse, straight, or right.

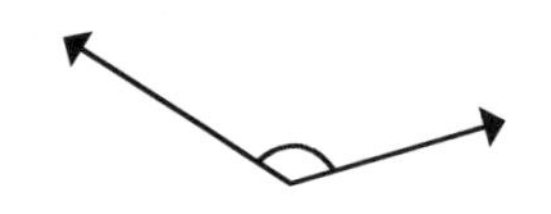

3. Draw and label an equilateral triangle.

4. How many lines of symmetry?

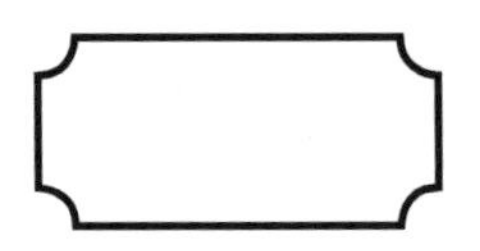

5. What is the measure of the missing angle?

39°

?

52°

THURSDAY Measurement

1. What is the perimeter of a hexagon with 2.5 m sides?

2. What is the area of a triangle with base 8 cm and height 15 cm?

3. Kaitlyn wants to practice the piano an extra 10 minutes each night in the month of March. How many minutes is that in total?

4. 330 L = ___ kL

5. Use the information to find the missing measure of the trapezoid.

height = 23.1 mm

b_1 = 27.3 mm

b_2 = 24.1 mm

area = __________

FRIDAY Data Management

Here is a double line graph showing weekend temperatures.

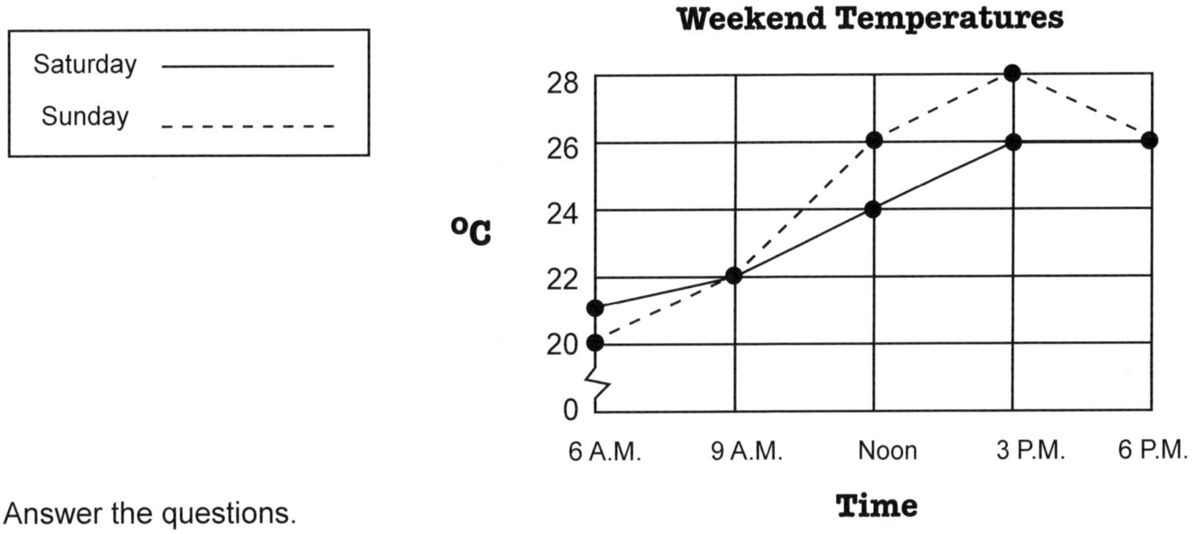

Weekend Temperatures

Time	Saturday (°C)	Sunday (°C)
6 A.M.		20
9 A.M.	22	22
Noon	24	26
3 P.M.	26	28
6 P.M.	26	26

Answer the questions.

1. What was the difference of temperatures at noon? ______________________

2. How much warmer was it at 3 p.m. on Sunday than it was at 3 p.m. on Saturday? __________

3. What was the range of temperature at noon? ______________________

4. When was the temperature the same on both Saturday and Sunday? ______________

5. What was the mean temperature on Sunday? ______________________

BRAIN STRETCH

If a cube with a 6 centimetre side length is sliced in half, what is the surface area of the two pieces?

MONDAY Patterning and Algebra

1. Extend the pattern. Start with 112.5; subtract 8.2 each time.

   112.5, ______, ______, ______

2. Predict what the 15th figure will be in this pattern.

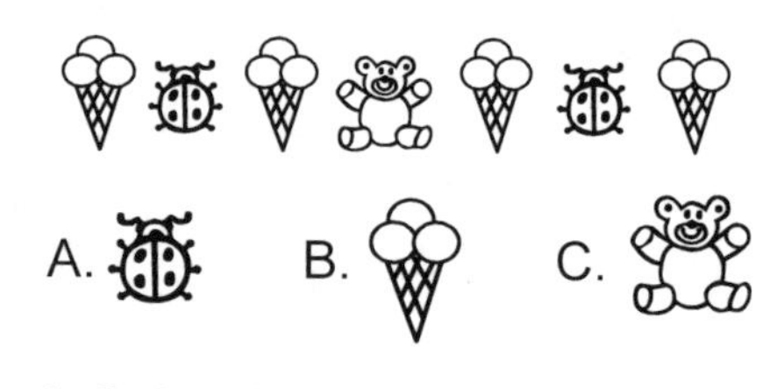

3. Express the phrase as an algebraic expression.

   quotient of a number c and 15

4. Solve the inequality.

   If $4X - 7 < -3$ Then $X <$ ____

5. Create a growing pattern. Write the rule.

TUESDAY Number Sense

1. Order the numbers from greatest to least.

   $\frac{2}{10}$, 0.354, 0.56

2. Name a prime number.

3. List all of the factors for the number:

   67

4. Complete.

   $-30 + (36 - 1 + -21 - -15) - -28$

5. Subtract. Write the answer in simplest form.

   $\frac{10}{12} - \frac{4}{6}$

WEDNESDAY Geometry

1. Name the shape.

2. Find the measure of the angle.

m < VAE = ____________

m < VAU = 30°

3. Draw a straight angle.

4. What 3D figure does this object resemble?

5. Draw and label an obtuse triangle.

THURSDAY Measurement

1. What is the perimeter of an equilateral triangle with 5.5 m sides?

2. Find the circumference.

   diameter = 51.68 cm

3. 94 300 cg = ___ g

4. What is the best unit of measure to measure how much water is in a pool?

5. Calculate the volume of a triangular prism to the nearest tenth.

   b = 13 cm^2 h = 5 cm

FRIDAY Data Management

Mrs. Poulos felt that a stop sign should be placed on the street in front of her house to stop cars from speeding down the road. She asked her daughter Demetra to survey the number of cars that drove past their home every day for an hour after school for five days. Here are her results.

Monday: 25 cars Tuesday: 18 cars Wednesday: 30 cars Thursday: 20 cars Friday: 45 cars

Complete the pictograph and answer the questions.

Day	Number of Cars
Monday	
Tuesday	
Wednesday	
Thursday	
Friday	

________ = ________ cars

Answer the questions.

1.	What day did the most cars travel past Mrs. Poulos' house?	**2.**	How many cars did Demetra count altogether?
3.	What was the range number of cars that passed her house each day after school?	**4.**	What the mean number of cars that drove past over five days?

What is the better buy?

A. 9 DVDs for $88 B. 21 DVDs for $168

MONDAY Patterning and Algebra

1. Express the phrase as an algebraic expression.

   a number *m* increased by 7

2. Create a shrinking pattern.

3. Solve for p.

   $p - 7 = 5^3 + 7$

4. Fill in the missing number.

   $82 - 63 \div \square = 75$

5. Follow the pattern rule. Start with the numbers 5 and 5; each number that follows is the sum of the two previous numbers.

   ________, ________, ________, ________, ________, ________,

TUESDAY Number Sense

1. Divide.

   $4\overline{)6.8}$

2. Write the percent as a fraction in simplest form.

   65%

3. Compare. Write <, >, or =.

   73 ________ 3341

4. Find the square root.

   $\sqrt{81}$

5. Add. Write the answer in simplest form.

   $4 + 19\frac{6}{13}$

WEDNESDAY Geometry

1. How many faces?

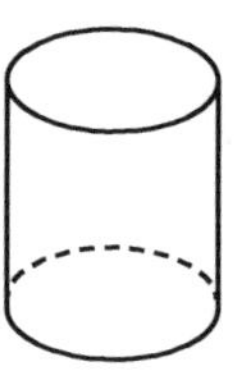

2. Classify the angle as acute, obtuse, straight, or right.

3. Draw a scalene triangle. Label the angles.

4. What is the measure of the missing angle?

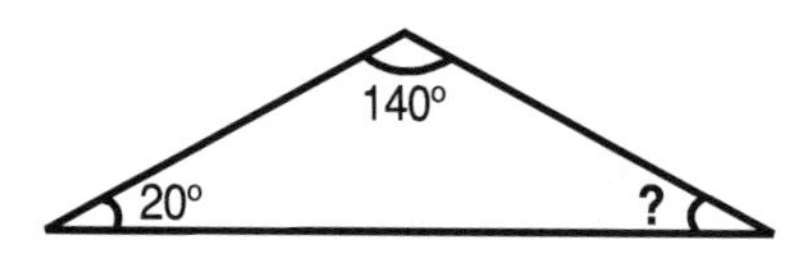

5. Draw a set of perpendicular lines.

THURSDAY Measurement

1. What is the height of a triangle with base 22 m and area 286 m^2?

2. Find the area of the circle. State your answer in terms of x and also round your answer to the nearest tenth.

   diameter = 4 m

3. 0.49 kL = _______ mL

4. How many litres are in 10 cans of 355 mL pop?

5. How many days in 2 leap years?

FRIDAY Data Management

This chart shows the stock prices for five different companies.

52 Week High	52 Week Low	Stock	Close
$34.67	$3.40	PSH	$26.78
$118.24	$96.62	ARC	$115.23
$55.71	$21.10	RAZ	$42.10
$65.34	$17.10	CHA	$48.22

1. Dave owns 2 shares of ARC and 1 share of RAZ. Using the closing price, how much are these shares worth?

2. How much more was PSH worth when it was at its 52 week high than its current closing price?

3. What was the range in price in 52 weeks for RAZ?

4. If you could own one of the stocks, which one would you choose? Explain your thinking.

BRAIN STRETCH

Do you think you are good at math? Explain your thinking.

MONDAY Patterning and Algebra

1. Create a growing pattern.
   Write the pattern rule.

2. Express the following problem algebraically.

   12 less than twice a number is 0

3. What number is missing from the following sequence?

   11, 22, 33, 44, _______, 66

4. Which of the following is an example of an inequality?

   A. 5n -6   B. 3n > 9   C. 6 + 2 = 8

5. Evaluate the expression where a = 10, and b = 6.

   (3b ÷ 3) + (a -5)

TUESDAY Number Sense

1. Subtract.

   $29 200.05
   \- 9 842.16

2. Write an integer to represent the description.

   13° above zero.

3. Complete the table. Numbers are rounded to the nearest hundredth of a percent.

fraction	decimal	percent
$\frac{5}{16}$	________	31.25%

4. What is the place value of the number in **bold**?

   1 **9**06 852

5. Write the improper fraction as a mixed number in simplest form.

   $\frac{132}{19}$

WEDNESDAY Geometry

1. Name a pair of complementary angles.

S, P, D, T, K, N

2. What 3D figure can you make from these pieces?

3. Draw and label an acute angle.

4. How many lines of symmetry?

6

5. What is the name of this 3D figure?

THURSDAY Measurement

1. What is the length of the base of a triangle with height 26.5 mm and area 367.025 mm^2?

2. Find the area of the circle. State your answer in terms of x and also round your answer to the nearest tenth.

   diameter = 45.04 m

3. 314.4 mm = _______ m

4. What would be the best unit of measure to measure the temperature outside?

5. Calculate the volume of a cylinder to the nearest tenth.

   d = 16 mm   h = 21 mm

FRIDAY Data Management

A hockey card was worth $5 when it was issued in 2004. The table shows the value of the card each year since 2004.

Year	Value of Card
2004	$5.00
2005	$5.30
2006	$5.65
2007	$6.05
2008	$6.50
2009	$7.00

Answer the questions:

1. Based on the information in the table, what is a reasonable prediction for the value of the baseball card 2013? Explain your thinking.

____

____

2. What kind of graph would you use to display the information in the table? Explain your thinking

____

3. In which year did the hockey card gain the most value? ____________

4. In which year did the hockey card gain the least value? ____________

BRAIN STRETCH

In four more years, Ben's grandfather will be five times as old as Ben was last year. When Ben's present age is added to his grandfather's present age, the total is 72. How old is each one now?

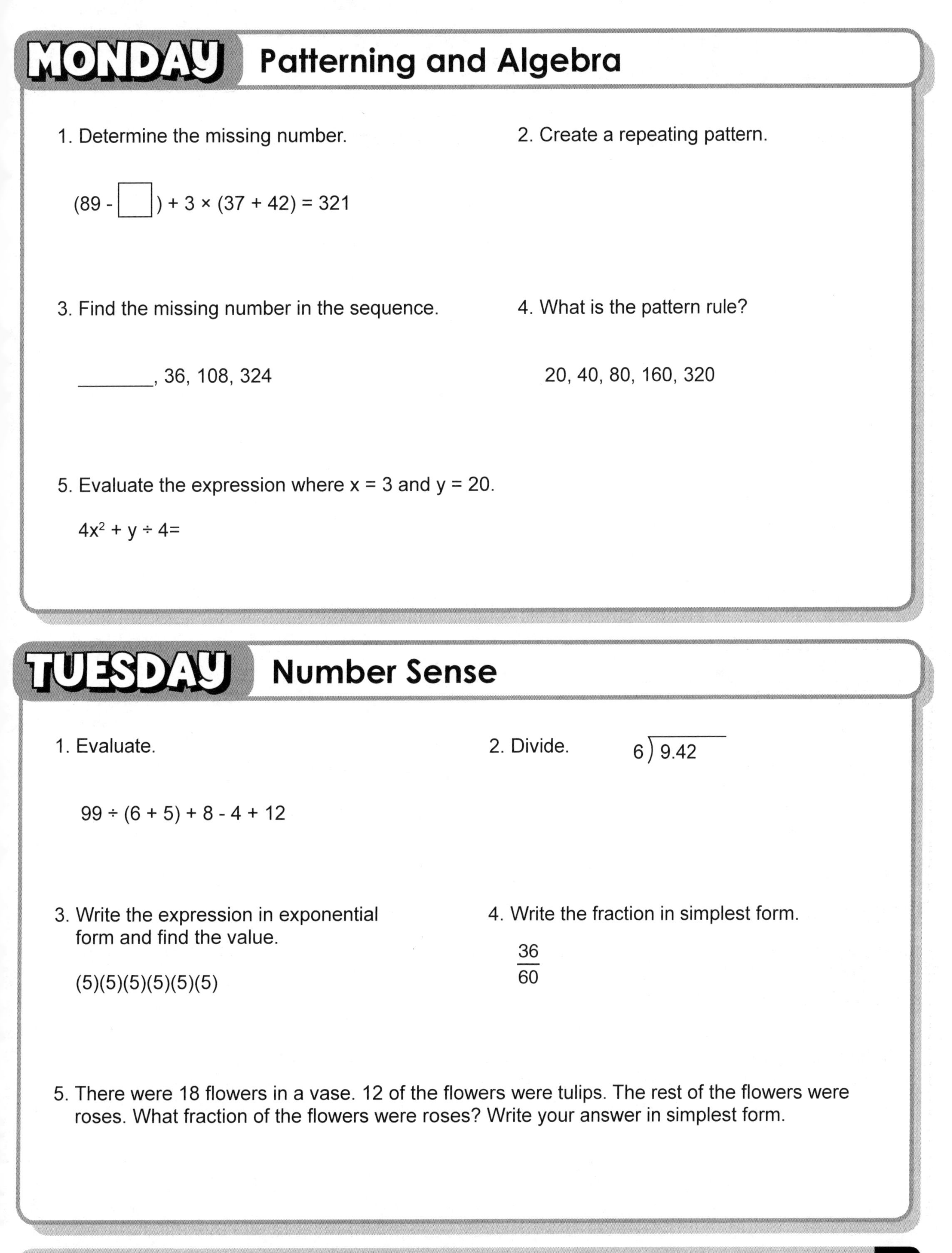

MONDAY Patterning and Algebra

1. Determine the missing number.

$(89 - \square) + 3 \times (37 + 42) = 321$

2. Create a repeating pattern.

3. Find the missing number in the sequence.

_______, 36, 108, 324

4. What is the pattern rule?

20, 40, 80, 160, 320

5. Evaluate the expression where x = 3 and y = 20.

$4x^2 + y \div 4 =$

TUESDAY Number Sense

1. Evaluate.

$99 \div (6 + 5) + 8 - 4 + 12$

2. Divide. $6\overline{)9.42}$

3. Write the expression in exponential form and find the value.

(5)(5)(5)(5)(5)(5)

4. Write the fraction in simplest form.

$\frac{36}{60}$

5. There were 18 flowers in a vase. 12 of the flowers were tulips. The rest of the flowers were roses. What fraction of the flowers were roses? Write your answer in simplest form.

WEDNESDAY Geometry

1. Draw an irregular decagon.

2. Find the measure of the angle.

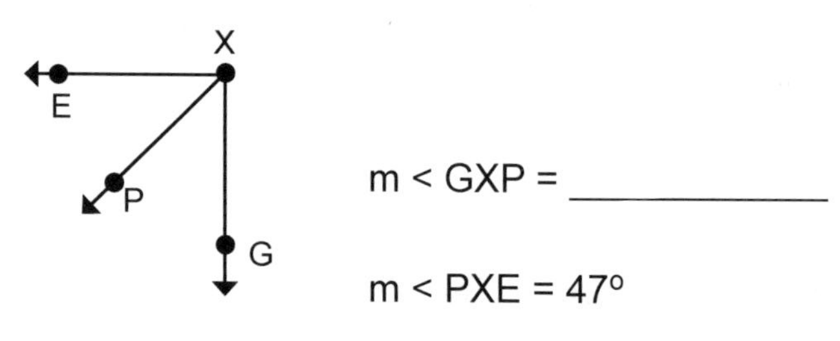

m < GXP = ____________

m < PXE = 47°

3. How many edges does a cone have?

4. Translate the shape.

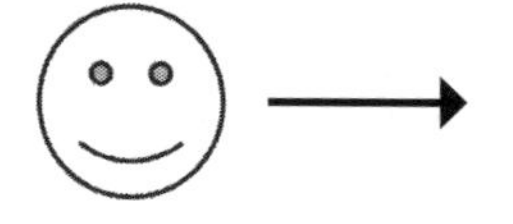

5. Draw and label an isosceles triangle.

THURSDAY Measurement

1. What is the perimeter of a heptagon with 12.1 m sides?

2. Order the metric measurements from least to greatest.

   5 mL; 0.7 cL; 83 000 L

3. 486 kg = _______ g

4. What time is 15:00 on the 12 hour clock?

5. Calculate the area of the parallelogram.

$\overline{AE}$ = 18.7 cm $\overline{AC}$ = 16.7 cm n = 16.3 cm

FRIDAY Data Management

Find the number of possible choices when you choose one item from each category.

1. 4 pants, 3 pairs of shoes, 6 shirts

2. 4 cars, 4 colours

3. 4 dinners, 5 drinks, 2 desserts

BRAIN STRETCH

Madelyn made a round picture frame that is 40 cm in diameter. She wanted to wrap a red ribbon around the outside of the frame three times. How long does the red ribbon need to be?

MONDAY Patterning and Algebra

1. Solve the inequality.

   If 6X + 4 < 34 Then X < _____

2. Create a growing pattern.

3. 783 + b = 907

   b = _____

4. Express the phrase as an algebraic expression.

   7 multiplied by a number e

5. Complete the function table. Rule: d = t + 5

Input	t	9	22		38
Output	d			41	

TUESDAY Number Sense

1. Multiply.

$$\begin{array}{r} 801 \\ \times\ 3.6 \\ \hline \end{array}$$

2. Write the decimal in words.

   0.092

3. Find the unit rate. Round your answer to the nearest hundredth

   $11.68 for 8 hour.

   ________ per hour

4. Put the integers in order from least to greatest.

   -26, 67, 45, 18, 38, -4, -3

5. Subtract. Write the answer in simplest form.

$$\frac{10}{12} - \frac{4}{6}$$

WEDNESDAY Geometry

1. What is the measure of the missing angle?

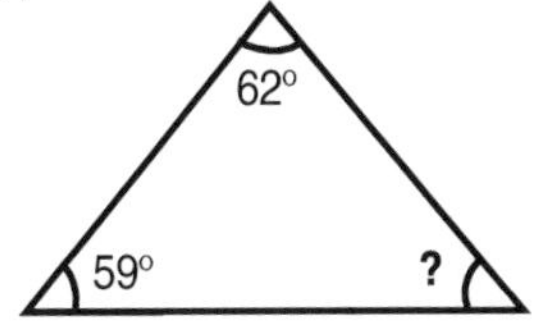

2. Classify the angle as *acute*, *obtuse*, *straight*, or *right*.

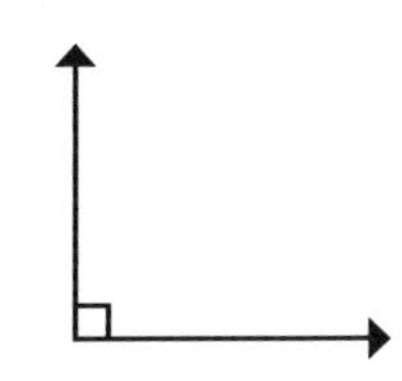

3. How many lines of symmetry?

E

4. Draw a set of intersecting lines.

5. What is the name of this 3D figure?

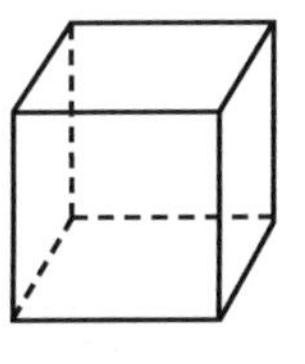

THURSDAY Measurement

How is measurement used in everyday life? Explain your thinking.

___

___

___

___

___

___

___

FRIDAY Data Management

Here is a circle graph that shows students' favourite snack. Use the information to answer the questions.

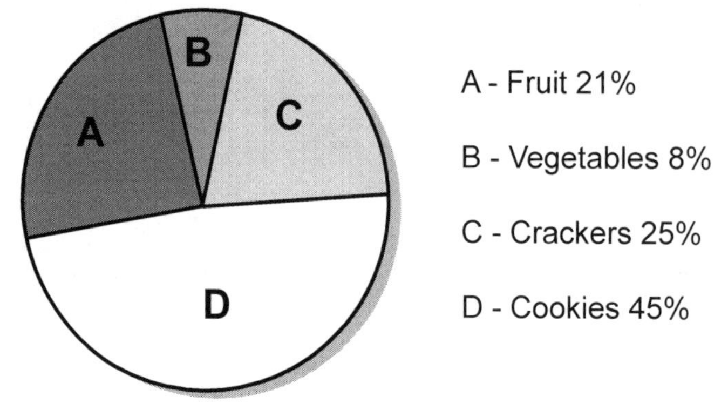

1. If the school has 230 students, how many students liked fruit the best? ______________

2. What fraction of the students liked crackers? ______________

3. What fraction of the students liked cookies? ______________

4. What percentage of students either liked fruit or crackers? ______________

5. What was the least popular snack? ______________

BRAIN STRETCH

A school parking lot had room for 100 parking spaces. 1/5 of the spaces were for bikes. On Tuesday, there were 20 bikes and some cars in the parking lot. 3/4 of the parking spaces were filled. How many cars were in the parking lot?

MONDAY Patterning and Algebra

1. Find the missing number in the sequence.

   2816, 704, 176, _____

2. Fill in the missing operation.

   58 ☐ 5 × 4 = 78

3. Find the inequality.

   If 3X - 9 < -6 Then X < _____

4. Create a growing pattern. Write the pattern rule.

5. Write the rule for the function table as an equation. Rule: ______________________

Input	a	7	14	21	28
Output	b	1	2	3	4

TUESDAY Number Sense

1. Rewrite the number in scientific notation.

   0.000033

2. Solve.

   774 - 389 =

3. List all of the factors for the number:

   46

4. Find the unit rate. Round your answer to the nearest hundredth.

   a 3.2 kg bag of cookies for $4.48

   ________ per kg

5. Multiply. Express the answer to the nearest thousandths.

   0.44 x 9

WEDNESDAY Geometry

1. How many lines of symmetry?

2. Draw a trapezoid.

3. What 3D figure could be made from these pieces?

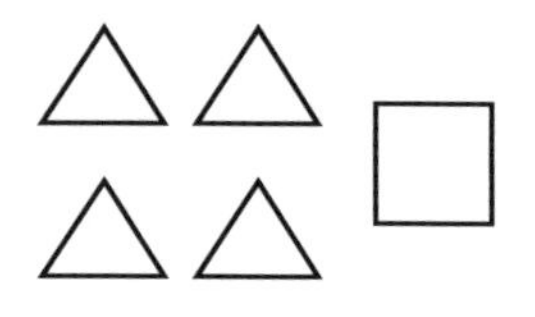

4. Find the measure of the angle.

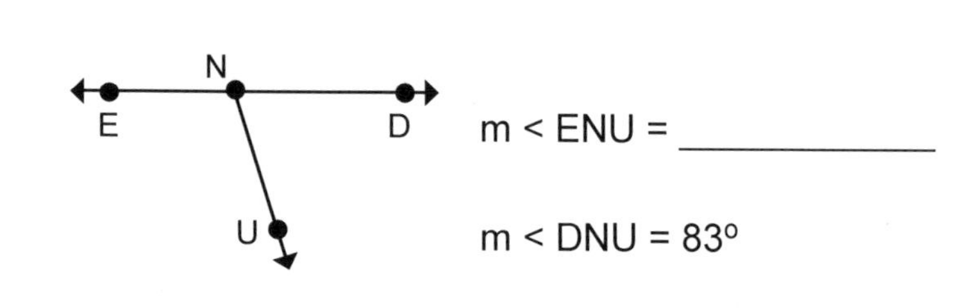

m < ENU = ______________

m < DNU = 83°

5. Classify this triangle as isosceles, scalene, or equilateral and as right, acute, or obtuse.

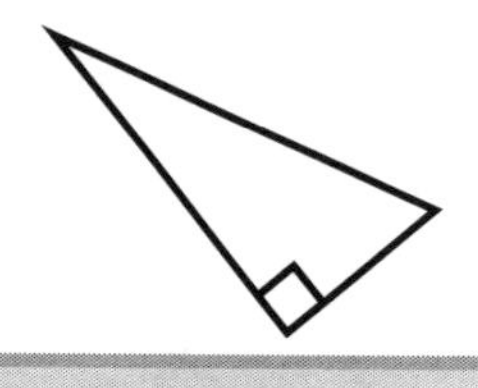

THURSDAY Measurement

1. The area of a rectangle is 150 mm^2. The height is five more than five times the base. What is the perimeter?

2. Order the metric measurements from least to greatest.

   0.6503 m; 40 cm; 5000 mm

3. How many days in a leap year?

4. Solve in kg.

   12 kg + 9 mg =

5. Calculate the volume of a triangular prism to the nearest tenth.

   b = 33 cm^2 h = 16 cm

FRIDAY Data Management

Michael earns $25 000 a year. Here are his monthly expenses.

Expenses	Amount
Apartment Rental	$1240
Car Payment	$400
School Loan	$280
Food	$700
Clothing	$120
Entertainment	$400
Other	$400

Answer the questions.

1. What percent of Michael's income is budgeted for the rental of his apartment?

2. After all of his expenses are paid how much money does Michael save each month?

3. What combined percentage of Michael's income is spent on car payment and school loan?

4. How much money does Michael spend on clothing in a year?

BRAIN STRETCH

How many squares do you see?

MONDAY Patterning and Algebra

1. Extend the pattern. Multiply by -2 then add 5.

   6, _______, _______, _______,

2. Create a shrinking pattern. Write the pattern rule.

3. Express the phrase as an algebraic expression.

   25 minus a number b

4. Evaluate the expression where $x = 8$ and $y = 12$.

   $(y^2 + y) \div (2 + x) =$

5. Write the rule for the function table as an equation. Rule: ____________________

Input	a	3	4	5	6
Output	b	12	16	20	24

TUESDAY Number Sense

1. Find the prime factorization for the number:

   56

2. Divide. $40\overline{)2240}$

3. Write an integer to represent the description.

   12 units to the left of – 23 on a number line.

4. Kaitlyn bought 4 bunches of tulips. Each bunch cost $4.20. She paid with $20.00. What was Kaitlyn's change?

5. Order the fractions from greatest to least.

   $\frac{2}{3}$, $\frac{1}{4}$, $\frac{5}{8}$

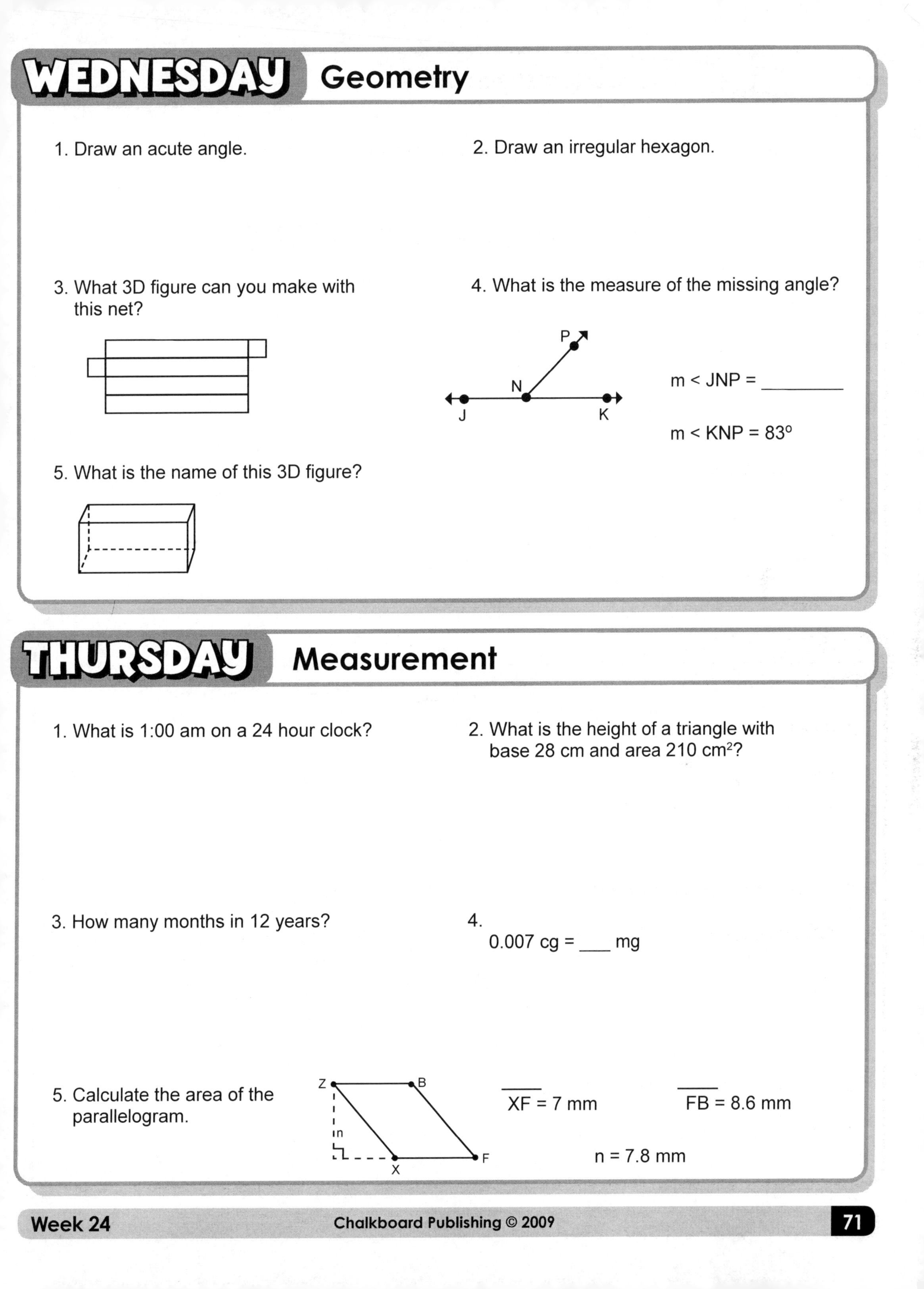

WEDNESDAY Geometry

1. Draw an acute angle.

2. Draw an irregular hexagon.

3. What 3D figure can you make with this net?

4. What is the measure of the missing angle?

m < JNP = ________

m < KNP = 83°

5. What is the name of this 3D figure?

THURSDAY Measurement

1. What is 1:00 am on a 24 hour clock?

2. What is the height of a triangle with base 28 cm and area 210 cm^2?

3. How many months in 12 years?

4.
0.007 cg = ___ mg

5. Calculate the area of the parallelogram.

$\overline{XF}$ = 7 mm

$\overline{FB}$ = 8.6 mm

n = 7.8 mm

FRIDAY Data Management

A group of friends had a ski race. Here are their finish times.

Ski Race Finish Times

Name	Finish Time in Seconds
Chris	33.3
Sophie	28.9
Elizabeth	31.8
Ross	32.6
Dave	29.4

Answer the questions.

1. What is the mean finish time?

2. What was the median finish time?

3. What was the difference in times between Ross and Elizabeth?

4. What was Sophie's finish time in minutes?

BRAIN STRETCH

If a napkin is folded in half two times and the resulting folded paper is a square with an area of 64 cm^2, what were the length and width of the napkin before it was folded?

MONDAY Patterning and Algebra

1. Find the missing number in the sequence.

   160, 80, _______, 20

2. Create a shrinking pattern. Write the pattern rule.

3. Express the phrase as an algebraic expression.

   9 less than the product of 11 and a number p

4. Fill in the missing operation.

   (90 ÷ 2 ☐ 32) = 1440

5. Evaluate the expression where x = 7 and y = 6

   $(x^2 + y) \div 2 =$

TUESDAY Number Sense

1. How many dimes are in 12 toonies?

2. Divide. $5\overline{)8.345}$

3. Round the number to the nearest tens.

   16 743

4. Complete.

   (45 + 3 - 38) + (18 - 43 + 33)

5. Subtract. Write the answer in simplest form.

   $\frac{17}{18} - \frac{7}{9}$

WEDNESDAY Geometry

1. What shape is this?

2. Classify the angle as acute, obtuse, straight, or right.

3. How many edges?

4. Draw a right angle.

5. Classify the triangle.

THURSDAY Measurement

1. What is the height of a triangle with base 22.9 m and area 209.535 m^2?

2. Order the metric measurements from least to greatest.

   0.007 mm; 40 m; 2,500 cm

3. Find the area of the circle. State your answer in terms of Π and also round your answer to the nearest tenth.

   radius = 12 m

4. 7 034 100 mg = __________ kg

5. Calculate the volume of a pyramid to the nearest tenth.

   b = 49 m^2 h = 18 m

FRIDAY Data Management

Ryerson Public School held their annual cookie sale. Here are the numbers of cookies sold.

Name	Number Sold
Oatmeal	276
Chocolate Chip	185
Double Chocolate	302
Vanilla Crème	230

1. What was the ratio oatmeal cookies sold to vanilla crème?

2. How many more double chocolate cookies were sold than chocolate chip?

3. What was the mean number of cookies sold?

4. If each cookie sold for $0.75, how much money was raised altogether?

BRAIN STRETCH

Stephen wanted to purchase a used car for $12 800. Stephen was given the option of paying $2000 down and $380 a month for 36 months on the installment plan. How much more would Stephen pay for the car on the installment plan?

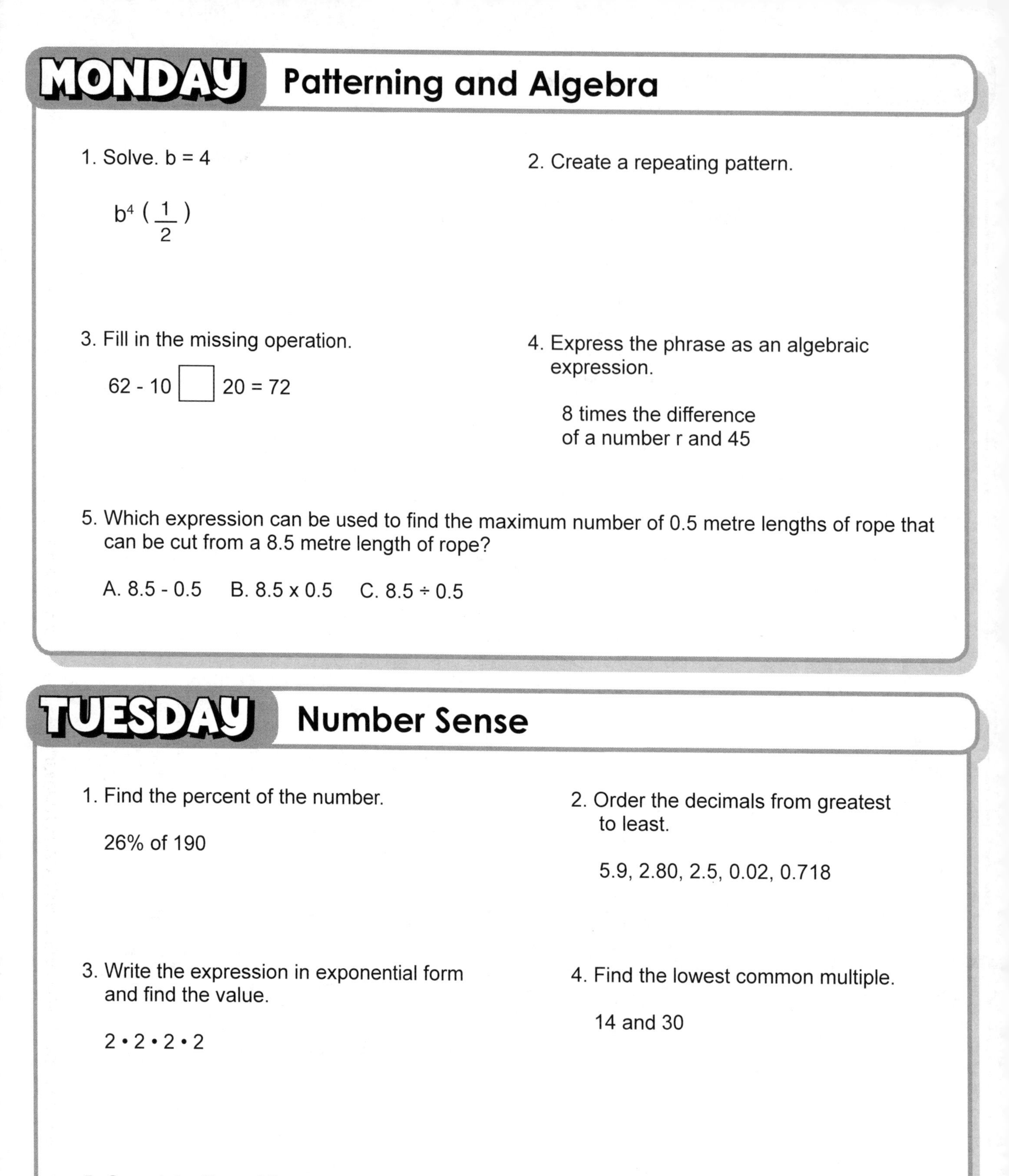

MONDAY Patterning and Algebra

1. Solve. $b = 4$

   $b^4 \left(\frac{1}{2}\right)$

2. Create a repeating pattern.

3. Fill in the missing operation.

   62 - 10 ☐ 20 = 72

4. Express the phrase as an algebraic expression.

   8 times the difference
   of a number r and 45

5. Which expression can be used to find the maximum number of 0.5 metre lengths of rope that can be cut from a 8.5 metre length of rope?

   A. 8.5 - 0.5 B. 8.5 x 0.5 C. 8.5 ÷ 0.5

TUESDAY Number Sense

1. Find the percent of the number.

   26% of 190

2. Order the decimals from greatest to least.

   5.9, 2.80, 2.5, 0.02, 0.718

3. Write the expression in exponential form and find the value.

   $2 \cdot 2 \cdot 2 \cdot 2$

4. Find the lowest common multiple.

   14 and 30

5. Complete. Round the answer to the nearest tenth.

   70 is 28% of what number?

WEDNESDAY Geometry

1. Find the measure of the angle..

m < JLS = __________

m < JLT = 136°

2. Draw a pair of similar shapes.

3. What 3D figure can you make from these pieces?

4. Draw an irregular heptagon.

5. How many lines of symmetry? **Q**

THURSDAY Measurement

1. Find the area of the triangle.

n = 31 cm

$\overline{YB}$ = 10 cm $\overline{BV}$ = 35 cm

$\overline{YV}$ = 31 cm

2. Solve in L.

122 mL + 5 L =

3. What time is 13:15 on the 12 hour clock?

4. What would be the best unit of measure to measure the time a person sleeps each night?

5.
0.7839 g = ________ mg

FRIDAY Data Management

Use the information below to complete the questions.

A																				
B																				
C																				
D																				
E																				

1. Which row shows 50% of the row is shaded? ______________________________

2. Which row shows less than 0.25 of the row is shaded? ______________________

3. What percent of row B is shaded? ______________________________

4. What is the ratio of row B shaded to row E? ______________________________

5. Which row is shaded between ¼ and ½? ______________________________

BRAIN STRETCH

If Kaitlyn jogs 2.5 km in 14 minutes, how far can she jog in half an hour in metres at the same rate?

MONDAY Patterning and Algebra

1. Create a growing pattern.
   Write a pattern rule.

2. Express the phrase as an algebraic expression.

   3 times the sum of a number g and 41

3. What will be the 9th number in this sequence?

   8, 80, 800, 8000

4. Find the inequality.

   If $10X - 4 > 56$ Then $X >$ _____

5. Complete the function table. Rule: $s = y^2 + 3$

Input	y	9	11	14	15
Output	s				

TUESDAY Number Sense

1. Complete the table. Numbers are rounded to the nearest hundredth of a percent.

fraction	decimal	percent
$\frac{3}{10}$	________	30%

2. Find the prime factorization for the number:

   30

3. Write the expression in exponential form and find the value.

   (6)(6)(6)

4. Divide. $2.4\overline{)54}$

5. Simpify.

   $(69 + 1) - (4 - 22 \times 3)$

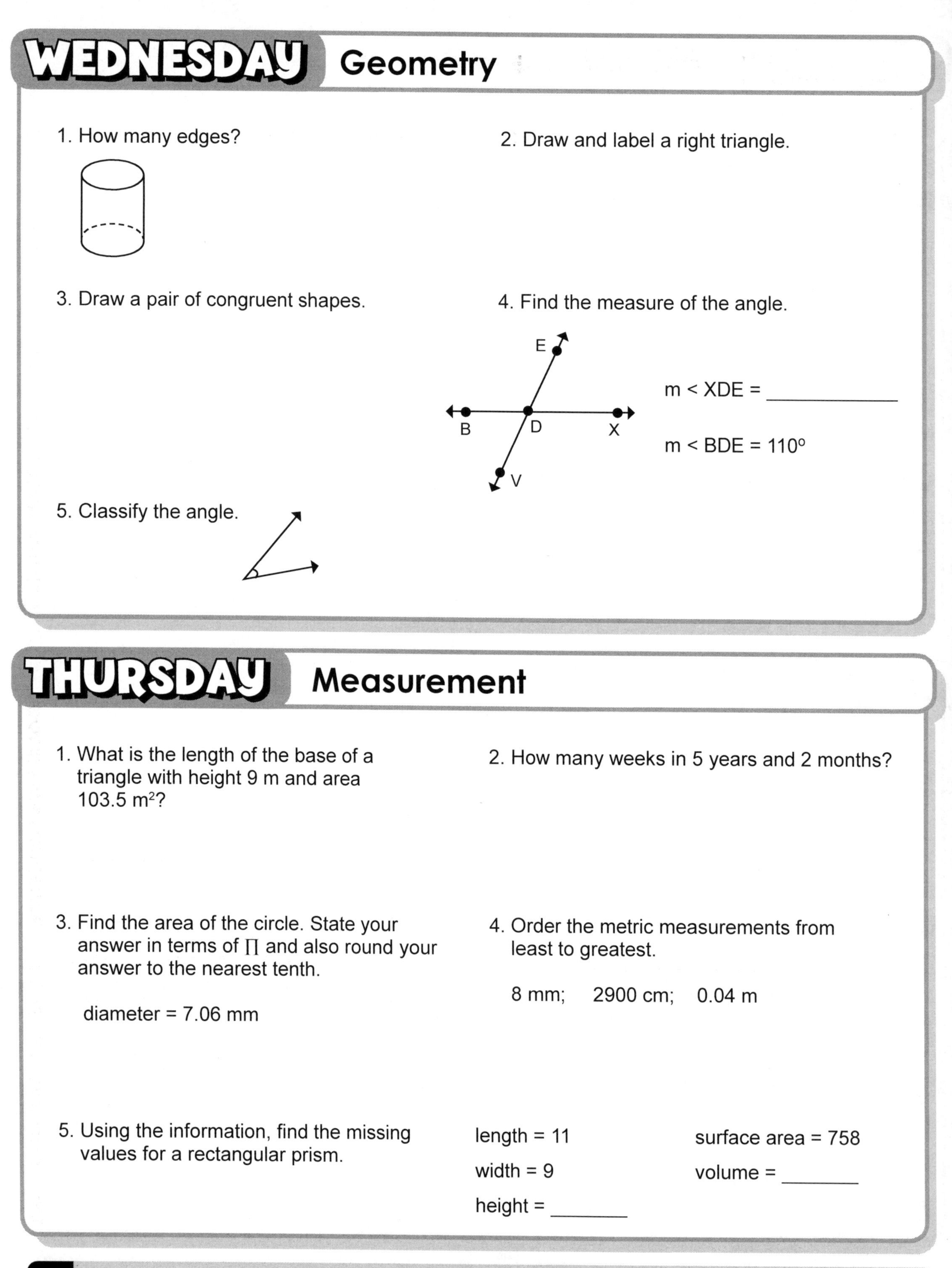

WEDNESDAY Geometry

1. How many edges?

2. Draw and label a right triangle.

3. Draw a pair of congruent shapes.

4. Find the measure of the angle.

m < XDE = ____________

m < BDE = 110°

5. Classify the angle.

THURSDAY Measurement

1. What is the length of the base of a triangle with height 9 m and area 103.5 m^2?

2. How many weeks in 5 years and 2 months?

3. Find the area of the circle. State your answer in terms of ∏ and also round your answer to the nearest tenth.

   diameter = 7.06 mm

4. Order the metric measurements from least to greatest.

   8 mm; 2900 cm; 0.04 m

5. Using the information, find the missing values for a rectangular prism.

   length = 11

   width = 9

   height = ________

   surface area = 758

   volume = ________

FRIDAY Data Management

Here is a chart to show how Bill spent a 24 hour period. Use the information given to complete the chart and answer the questions.

How 24 Hours Are Spent

Activity	Time	Hours
a. sleeping	1/3 of the time	
b. at meals	1/12 of the time	
c. at school	2/6 of the time	
d. on the Internet	1/24 of the time	
e. on phone/texting	1/24 of the time	
f. at sports practice	1/24 of the time	
g. relaxing	1/12 of the time	
h. exercising	1/24 of the time	

1. At what activity or activities did Bill spend the most amount of time? ____________________

2. How many hours did Bill spend on the internet and relaxing? ____________________

3. At what activities did Bill spend equally? ____________________

BRAIN STRETCH

Spencer earned $19.33 on a principal of $511 after 2 years. What was the simple interest rate? Round your answer to the nearest hundredth of a percent.

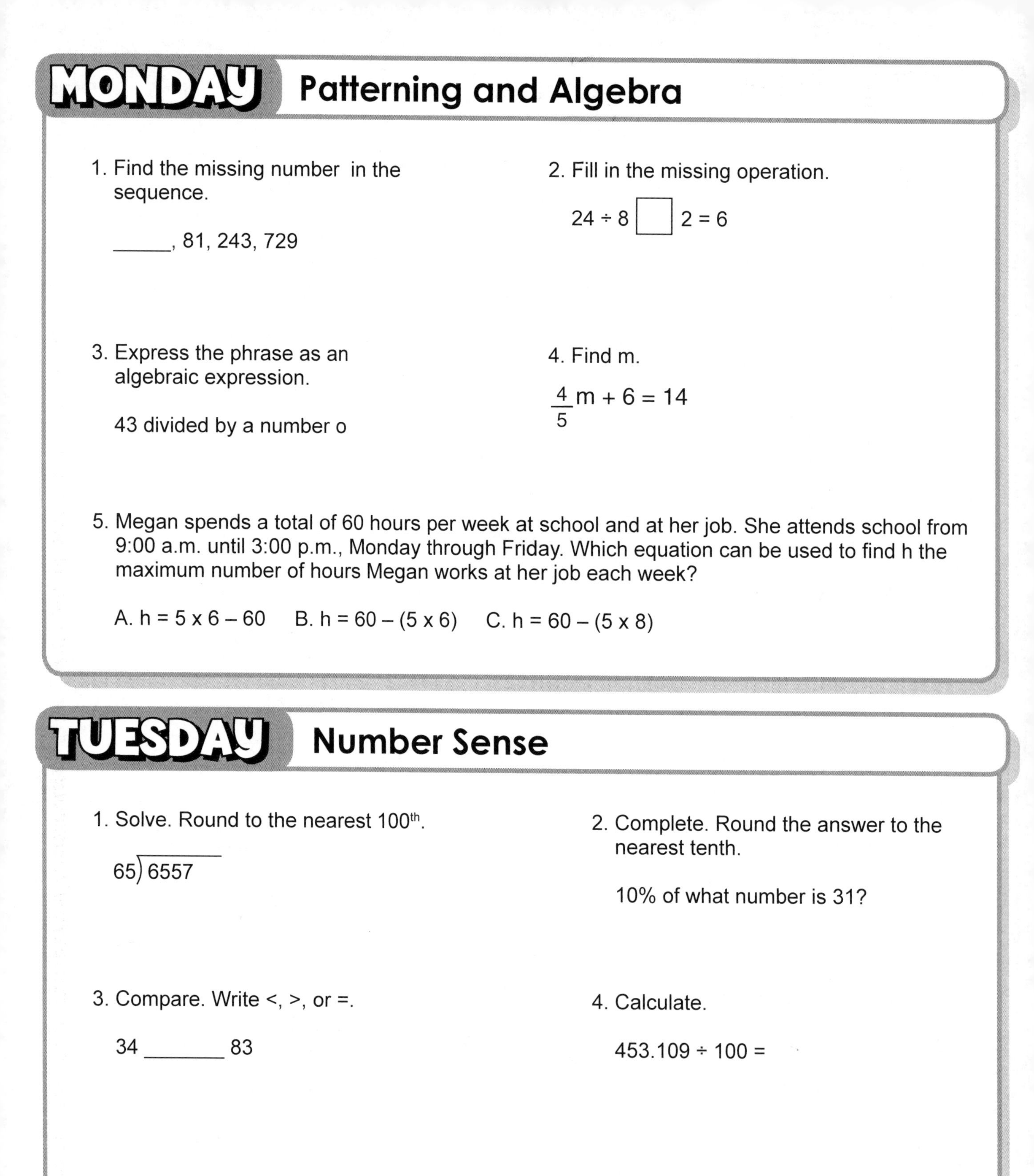

MONDAY Patterning and Algebra

1. Find the missing number in the sequence.

   _____, 81, 243, 729

2. Fill in the missing operation.

   24 ÷ 8 ☐ 2 = 6

3. Express the phrase as an algebraic expression.

   43 divided by a number o

4. Find m.

   $\frac{4}{5}m + 6 = 14$

5. Megan spends a total of 60 hours per week at school and at her job. She attends school from 9:00 a.m. until 3:00 p.m., Monday through Friday. Which equation can be used to find h the maximum number of hours Megan works at her job each week?

   A. h = 5 x 6 – 60 B. h = 60 – (5 x 6) C. h = 60 – (5 x 8)

TUESDAY Number Sense

1. Solve. Round to the nearest 100th.

   $65\overline{)6557}$

2. Complete. Round the answer to the nearest tenth.

   10% of what number is 31?

3. Compare. Write <, >, or =.

   34 ________ 83

4. Calculate.

   453.109 ÷ 100 =

5. Write an integer to represent the description.

   a raise of $500

WEDNESDAY Geometry

1. What is the measure of the missing angle?

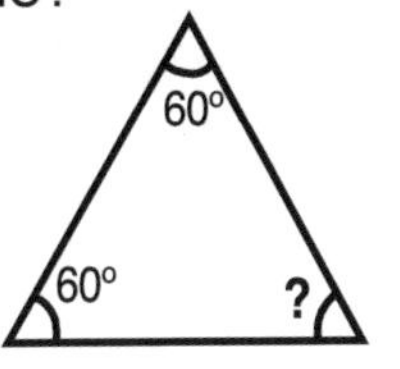

2. How many faces?

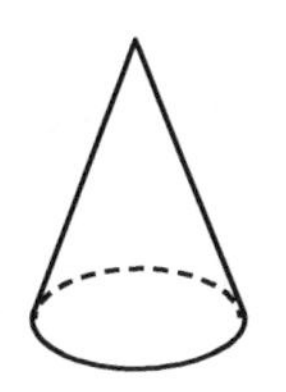

3. Is a rhombus a rectangle?

4. Draw a pair of intersecting lines.

5. Draw a scalene triangle.

THURSDAY Measurement

1. What is the best unit of measure to measure the width of a finger?

2. What is the length of the base of a triangle with height 10 mm and area 75 mm^2?

3. How many days in a millennium?

4. 304 cg = __________ mg

5. What is the elapsed time?

   7:15 a.m. to 4:23 p.m.

FRIDAY Data Management

Survey of family sizes at Tecumseh School

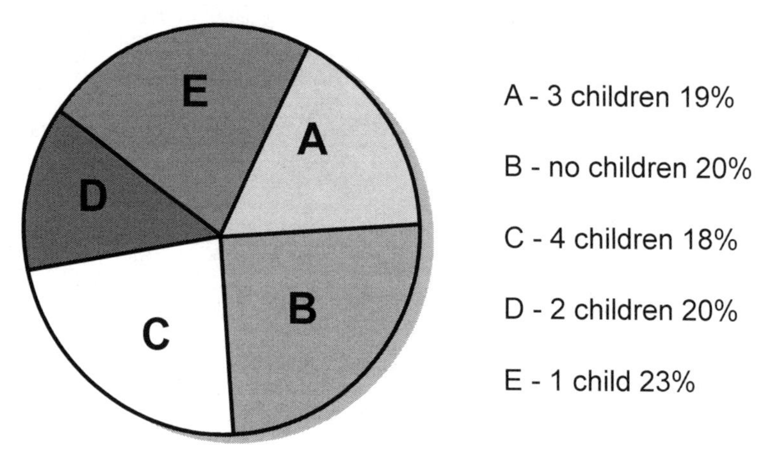

Answer the questions using the information from the pie graph.

1.	What is the ratio of families that have 4 children to 1 child?	**2.**	If 152 families were surveyed, list the how many families have either 4 children or 2 children.
3.	If 152 families were surveyed, how many fewer families have 3 children than those that have 1 child?	**4.**	What is the ratio of families that have 3 children to no children?

BRAIN STRETCH

Sophie bought 4 T-shirts. Each T-shirt cost $32.50. How much did the T-shirts cost altogether? She paid with a $50 bill and 10 toonies. Did she get change? Explain.

MONDAY Patterning and Algebra

1. Create a repeating pattern.

2. Express the following problem algebraically.

   6 less than the product of 9 and a number is 30

3. Combine like terms.

   $7k - 13k^2 - 2 - 3k + 15k^2$

4. What number comes next in the sequence?

   32, 128, 512, _______

5. Write the rule for the function table as an equation. Rule: _______________________

Input	a	25	30	35	40
Output	b	5	6	7	8

TUESDAY Number Sense

1. Complete.

   33 ÷ 3 - 34 - 49

2. Rewrite the number in scientific notation.

   0.0005

3. Write an integer to represent the description.

   A loss of $452 on an investment.

4. Order the fractions from least to greatest.

   $\frac{5}{6}$, $\frac{3}{4}$, $\frac{1}{2}$

5. Find the least common multiple.

   3, 9, and 21

WEDNESDAY Geometry

1. Draw a pair of similar shapes.

2. Classify the angle as acute, obtuse, straight, or right.

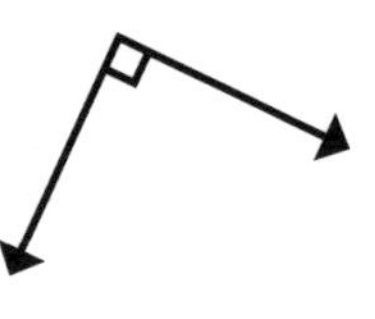

3. What 3D figure could be made from these pieces?

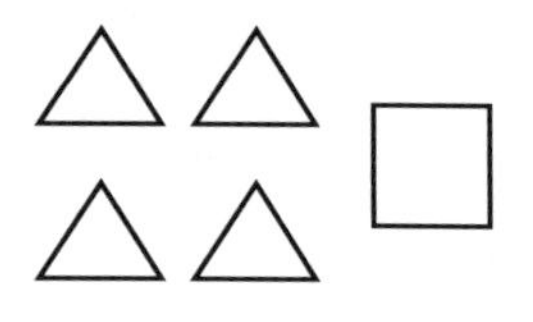

4. Define the term obtuse angle.

5. Draw a shape with at least three lines of symmetry.

THURSDAY Measurement

1. Find the area of the circle. State your answer in terms of Π and also round your answer to the nearest tenth.

   diameter = 18 mm

2. 861 kg = ______________ g

3. What time is 20:30 on the 12 hour clock?

4. What would be the best unit of measure to measure the time to brush your teeth?

5. Using the information, find the missing values for a rectangular prism.

   length = 5

   width = 12

   height = ________

   surface area = ________

   volume = 600

FRIDAY Data Management

The table below shows the number of students in each grade at Parkdale Middle School who are enrolled in various clubs.

Club	Grade 7	Grade 8	Grade 9
Drama	12	12	10
Choir	50	44	52
Art	34	22	30
Newspaper	22	14	20

1. What kind of graph would you create to best display the data? Explain your thinking.

2. Which grade had the highest mean of students involved in clubs?

3. What was the ratio of students involved in clubs from 8th grade to 7th grade?

4. How many students were involved in art?

BRAIN STRETCH

Megan wanted to bake some muffins for a fundraiser. The recipe for a dozen muffins called for 1 1/2 cups of milk, 2 1/4 cups of flour, and 1 1/3 cups of other ingredients.
How many cups of milk, flour, and other ingredients are needed to make 4 dozen muffins?

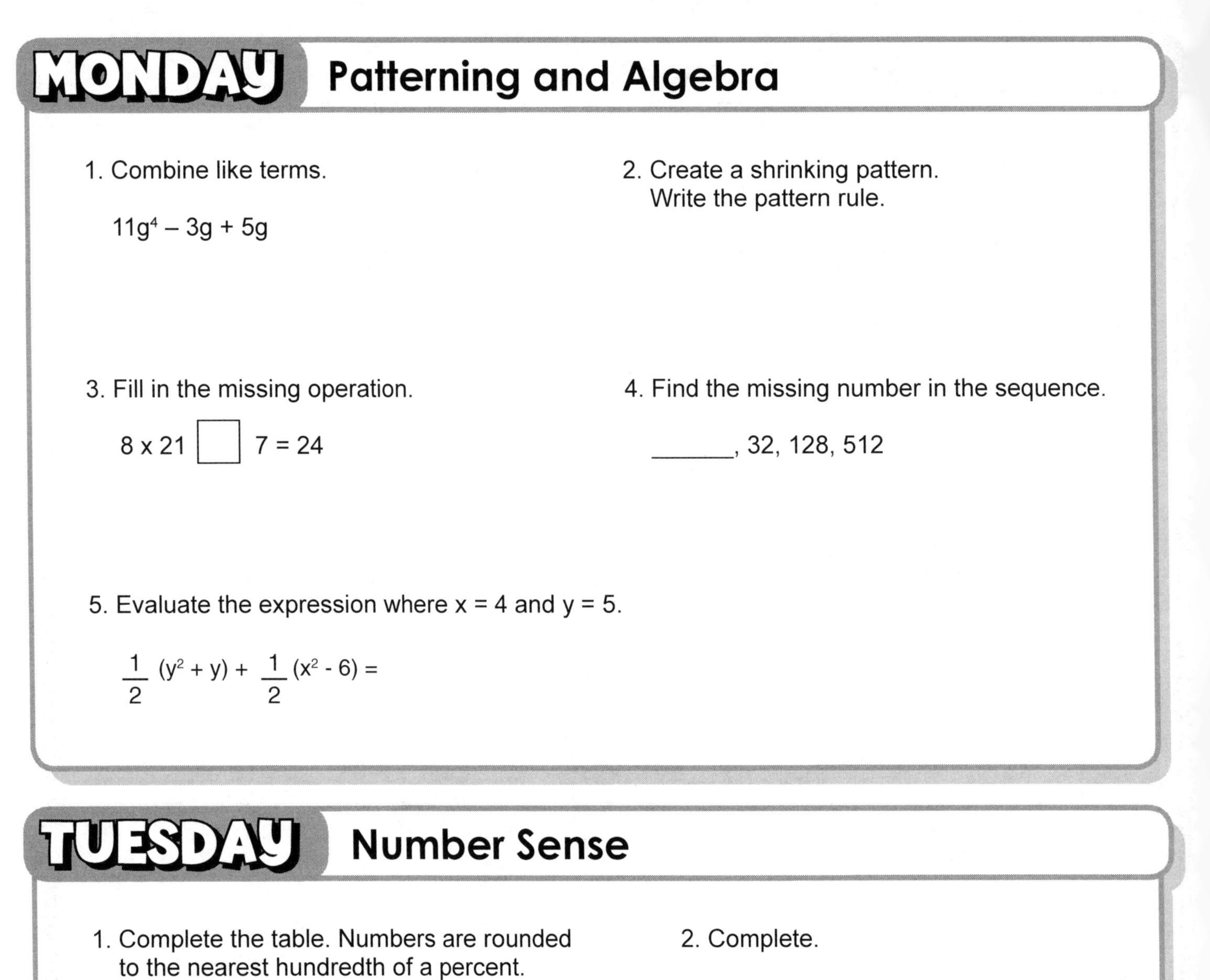

MONDAY Patterning and Algebra

1. Combine like terms.

   $11g^4 - 3g + 5g$

2. Create a shrinking pattern. Write the pattern rule.

3. Fill in the missing operation.

   8 x 21 ☐ 7 = 24

4. Find the missing number in the sequence.

   ______, 32, 128, 512

5. Evaluate the expression where x = 4 and y = 5.

   $\frac{1}{2}(y^2 + y) + \frac{1}{2}(x^2 - 6) =$

TUESDAY Number Sense

1. Complete the table. Numbers are rounded to the nearest hundredth of a percent.

fraction	decimal	percent
________	________	80%

2. Complete.

   -12 + 23 - 31- 35 +21

3. List all of the factors for the number:

   75

4. Write the mixed number as an improper fraction in simplest form.

   $6\frac{10}{17}$

5. Simplify.

   $(36 \div 4) \times 37 + (22 + 5)$

WEDNESDAY Geometry

1. Name the shape.

2. Draw an irregular decagon.

3. Draw and label a scalene triangle.

4. Draw a pair of congruent shapes.

5. Name part of the circle.

N H A P Y

$\overline{HN}$

THURSDAY Measurement

1. What is the height of a triangle with base 26 m and area 65 m^2?

2. What be the best unit of measure to measure how long it takes to have a drink at a fountain?

3. What time is 22:45 on the 12 hour clock?

4. Order the metric measurements from least to greatest.

80 m; 350 mm; 0.3 cm;

5. Using the Pythagorean Theorem, find the missing length of a right triangle. Simplify your answer.

a = 9

b = 21

c = __________

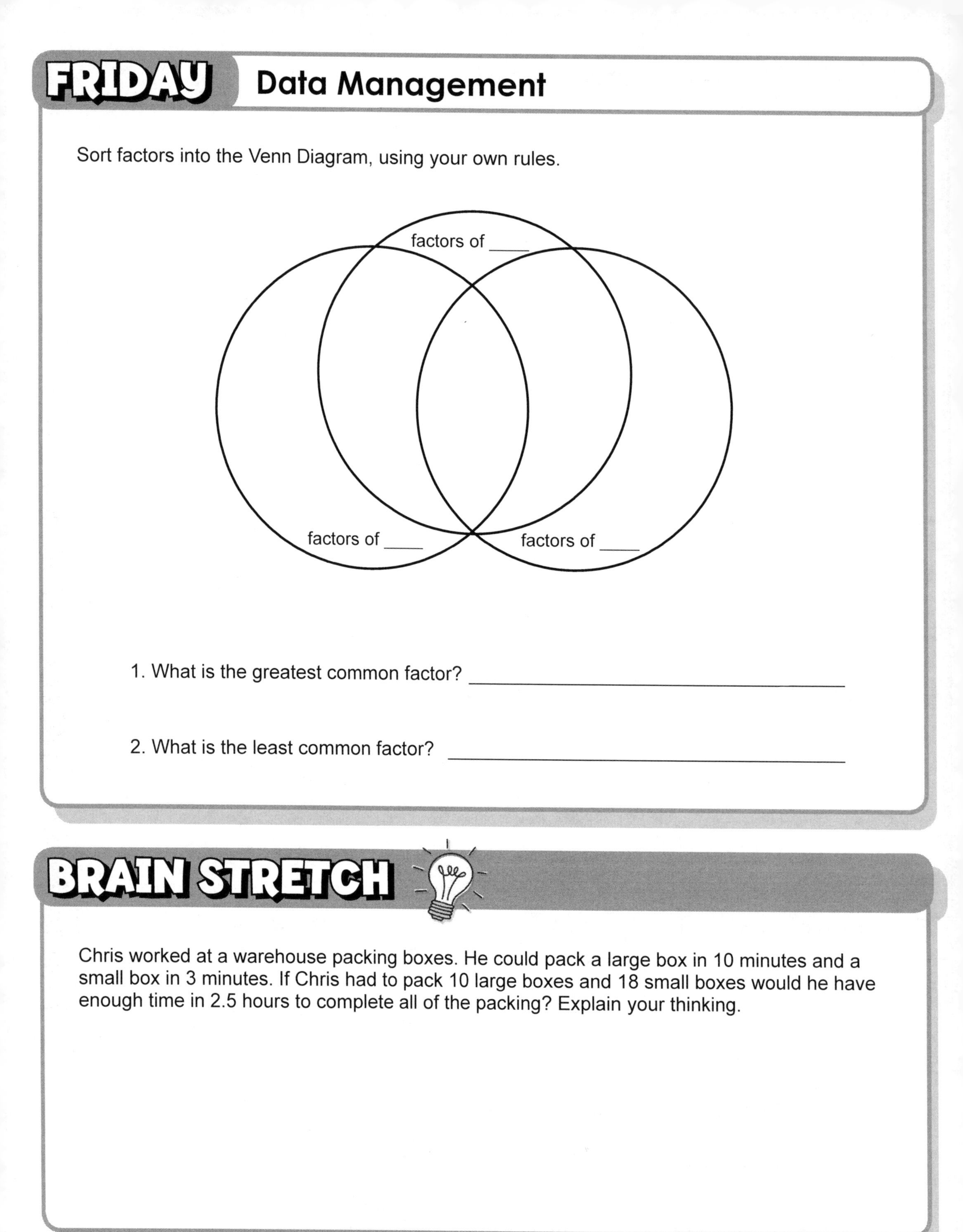

FRIDAY Data Management

Sort factors into the Venn Diagram, using your own rules.

1. What is the greatest common factor? ______________________

2. What is the least common factor? ______________________

BRAIN STRETCH

Chris worked at a warehouse packing boxes. He could pack a large box in 10 minutes and a small box in 3 minutes. If Chris had to pack 10 large boxes and 18 small boxes would he have enough time in 2.5 hours to complete all of the packing? Explain your thinking.

Math — Show What You Know!

____

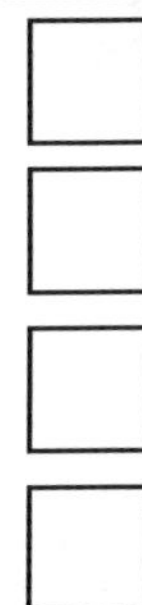

I read the question and I know what I need to find.

I drew a picture or a diagram to help solve the question.

I showed all the steps in solving the question.

I used math language to explain my thinking.

Student Tracking Sheet

Student	Week 1	Week 2	Week 3	Week 4	Week 5	Week 6	Week 7	Week 8	Week 9	Week 10	Week 11	Week 12	Week 13	Week 14	Week 15

Student Tracking Sheet

Student	Week 16	Week 17	Week 18	Week 19	Week 20	Week 21	Week 22	Week 23	Week 24	Week 25	Week 26	Week 27	Week 28	Week 29	Week 30

Student Certificate

Week 1

P1 **Mon** 1. 32 2. five plus m 3. Add 5 4. 140 5. 60

Tues 1. 2301 2. 64 3. 16 4. six hundred eighty nine thousand, four hundred twenty seven 5. 5/8

P2 **Wed** 1. 8 2. straight 3. square, rectangle, parallelogram, etc 4. answers will vary 5. one

Thurs 1. $75 m^2$ 2. C=50.24 m 3. 5997 mm 4. 22 800 sec 5. ml

P3 **Fri** 1. 24-79 2. Tigers 3. 58.4 4. 60 5. bar graph

Brain Stretch 2.8 cents

Week 2

P4 **Mon** 1. 0.000 000 07 2. 32 3. Add 5 4. three n minus 2 5. 182

Tues 1. 7205 2. 18/25 3. 48 4. 13 5. 7/8

P5 **Wed** 1. diameter 2. angle of less than 90° 3. isosceles 4. 60° 5. cylinder

Thurs 1. 15 cm 2. 5 hours 3. 107.45 m 4. 783.9 mg 5. $14.85 m^2$

P6 **Fri** 1. 11,9,3 2. 13,10,22 3. 14,15,7 4. 14,14,14

Brain Stretch $2.69

Week 3

P7 **Mon** 1. 11, 17, 23, 29 2. 19 3. Add 6 4. 4 5. 57

Tues 1. 55.19 2. hundreds 3. 45 4. $6.30 5. 192

P8 **Wed** 1. the same in every way 2. answers will vary 3. answers will vary 4. 30° 5. one

Thurs 1. 36 cm 2. $150 m^2$ 3. 2252 days 4. 30.4 mg 5. kg

P9 **Fri** 2. 7 3. 7

Brain Stretch 1. 208 2. 832 3. 37 440

Week 4

P10 **Mon** 1. 44,46,48,50 2. 15 3. 42 4. 729 5. 1/2L – 4 cm.

Tues 1. 3 1/3 2. 5 3. 35 4. 23 6/13 5. -7

P11 **Wed** 1. answers will vary 2. cube 3. answers will vary 4. two sides are of equal length 5. <YMP, <PMJ

Thurs 1. 9.002 kg 2. 25 cm 3. 71.6 cm 4. 2 hr 44 min 5. km

P12 **Fri** 1. Spinner 1 2. Spinner 2 3. Spinner 1 4. Letter D

Brain Stretch 45

Week 5

P13 **Mon** 1. two b divide by 2 2. 77 3. X 4. repeating 5. 51, 199, 791

Tues 1. 34 982 2. 275.52 3. 15 4. 70.0% 5. 23/18

P14 **Wed** 1. angles all the same 2. obtuse 3. ▱ 4. six 5. none

Thurs 1. 26.4 mm 2. 48.42 mm 3. 176 days 4. 0.877 cg 5. weights are equal

P15 **Fri** 1. 22-70 2. Class C 3. Class F 4. 34:44 5. 34

Brain Stretch 230

Week 6

P16 **Mon** 1. answers will vary 2. 12 3. B 4. add 50 5. 118

Tues 1. +120 2. twenty three hundredths 3. $7X10^3 + 8X10^2 + 1X10^1 + 4X10^0$ 4. B 5. 1/8 2/5 2/4

P17 **Wed** 1. 8 2. cone 3. all sides are equal in length 4. 40° 5. isosceles triangle

Thurs 1. 59.5 cm^2 2. 54.2 m 3. 9:30 p.m. 4. 4 hr 39 min 5. 24 cm

P18 **Fri** 1. answers will vary 2. answers will vary 3. answers will vary

Brain Stretch 0.72 kg

Week 7

P19 **Mon** 1. n – 56 = 61 2. answers will vary 3. 1701 4. 32 5. 3,4,5,6

Tues 1. $4234.58 2. 1400 3. $6 X 10^5$ 4. 20.09 5. 22/35

P20 **Wed** 1. 90° angle 2. 5 3. 7 4. answers will vary 5. chord

Thurs 1. 902 mm^2 2. 11 cm 3. 0.000 02345 kg 4. 132.88 mm 5. 6240 weeks

P21 **Fri** 1. answers will vary 2. answers will vary

Brain Stretch 1st day 0.50 cm 2nd day 0.95 cm

Week 8

P22 **Mon** 1. 4 2. 15 3. 47 – p 4. 2222222 5. 54

Tues 1. $3 X 10^3 + 3 X 10^2 + 3 X 10^1 + 4 X 10^0$ 2. 54.72 3. 9, 561, 605 4. 80.478 5. 1/2 5/14 3/9

P23 **Wed** 1. one angle is 90° 2. right 3. right scalene 4. six 5. <LVC and <JVM

Thurs 1. 23.79 cm^2 2. 11 hr 27 min 3. 1197 cL 4. m 5. 76.5 cm^2

P24 **Fri** 1. ~22 2. 23/100 3. 52/100 4. 41% 5. bus

Brain Stretch 1/3

Week 9

P25 **Mon** 1. 2 2. n = 5 3. 2025 4. -57, 339, -2037 5. 19, 27, 28, 41

Tues 1. 1, 5, 7 2. ¼, 0.3375, 0.3625 3. 42 4. C 5. 37/24

P26 **Wed** 1. answers will vary 2. 96° 3. an angle of 180° 4. four 5. radius

Thurs 1. 2:20 pm 2. 1 200 005 cL 3. -3 °C 4. 146 000 5. 6m X 6m

P27 **Fri** 1. answers will vary

Brain Stretch $21.25

Week 10

P28 **Mon** 1. -7, 26, -73 2. answers will vary 3. 6, 30, 150 4. p = 2 5. 93

Tues 1. $1X10^6 + 4X10^5 + 9X10^4 + 5X10^3 + 3X10^2 + 2X10^1 + 1X10^0$ 2. 12.325 3. 13, 3, 2, 1 4. 897 5. 2/3, 5/8, 1/4

P29 **Wed** 1. 12 2. 25° 3. parallelogram 4. answers will vary 5. equilateral

Thurs 1. 420.5 cm^2 2. 119.32 cm 3. 0.0009 mg 4. 125 m^3 5. 2880 m^3

P30 **Fri** 1. B 2. F 3. I 4. D 5. J 6. H 7. C 8. A 9. E 10. G

Brain Stretch Case is better buy at $2.11 per 6.

Week 11

P31 **Mon** 1. x + 2 = 37 2. g = 9 3. 88 4. 3 5. 27, 64, 125, 2126

Tues 1. 1880 2. 610 3. answers will vary 4. 3 5. 29/30

P32 **Wed** 1. semi-chord 2. answers will vary 3. <FPE and <GPE 4. answers will vary 5. answers will vary

Thurs 1. 86 400 seconds 2. 595 km 3. mm 4. 10 hr 25 min 5. 3627 m^2

P33 **Fri** 1. 100 2. 13.8 3. 65 4. 33

Brain Stretch Rob is faster, averaging 25.2 sec. for each 100m

Week 12

P34 **Mon** 1. 5.5 2. variable 3. + 4. 243 5. 2.5, 11.0, 19.5

Tues 1. 2×10^5 2. 12 3. 7390, 7400, 7408, 7501 4. A 5. 1/16

P35 **Wed** 1. triangle 2. obtuse 3. one 4. 68° 5. scalene

Thurs 1. 23 cm 2. 94.2 cm 3. 1200 months 4. mg 5. 71.89 mm^2

P36 **Fri** 1. Feb-Mar 2. April 3. 12 cm 4. 12 cm 5. 8 cm

Brain Stretch -6°C

Week 13

P37 **Mon** 1. -9 2. five n plus nine 3. m-5 4. 0.05, 2.55, 5.05 5. 54

Tues 1. 11 2. 63 3. 100 4. ten thousands 5. 13

P38 **Wed** 1. parallelogram 2. 53° 3. cylinder 4. one 5. <QBM & <MBS

Thurs 1. 11.9994 kg 2. 137.03 cm 3. 0.007 m 4. 1350 min 5. 8.62 cm

P39 **Fri** 1. 6 cm 2. 10.9 cm 3. 12 cm 4. Plant #1

Brain Stretch 6:48 p.m.

Week 14

P40 **Mon** 1.variable 2. 27 3. A 4. 76, 835, 9184 5. 25,30,35,40

Tues 1. 54.72 2. ten thousands 3. ¾ 4. 576 5. 8

P41 **Wed** 1. answers will vary

Thurs 1. 14:00 2. 157.44 mm^2 3. 3457 mL 4. 11.996 km 5. 3600 min

P42 **Fri** 1. Games 1&4 2. 200-450 3. 275 4. 1100 5. Game 2

Brain Stretch 41

Week 15

P43 **Mon** 1. 17 2. answers will vary 3. 17 – p = 6 4. 81 5. 41

Tues 1. 7, 1 2. 729 3. 4 7/10 4. 34 5. $31 868.44

P44 **Wed** 1. triangle with no 2 sides equal 2. rectangular prism 3. answers will vary 4. m<KUN= 99° 5. cylinder

Thurs 1. 1980 sec 2. 0.00049 km 3. 20:00 4. 7 hr 10 min 5. 74 m

P45 **Fri** 1. bar 2. circle 3. Line 4. Scatter Plot 5. Pictograph 6. Double Bar

Brain Stretch 1.29 m high

Week 16

P46 **Mon** 1. 21 2. variable 3. 12 4. n=20 5. 72.8, 70.6, 68.4

Tues 1. 60 000 2. $93 896.49 3. 91, 1 4. C 5. 13/77

P47 **Wed** 1. 6 2. answers will vary 3. answers will vary 4. rectangular prism 5. <YAZ & <ZAS

Thurs 1. 24 m 2. 144.44 cm 3. 73 100 cL 4. kg 5. 35.26 cm^2

P48 **Fri** 1. answers will vary

Brain Stretch 240 mm

Week 17

P49 **Mon** 1. C 2. $1524 3. 160 4. -2 5. 1, 2, 6, 5

Tues 1. 31.32 2. 11X2 3. 84 4. 2 5/16 5. $3^5 = 243$

P50 **Wed** 1. 12 2. obtuse 3. answers will vary 4. two 5. 89°

Thurs 1. 15 m 2. 60 cm^2 3. 310 min 4. 0.33 kL 5. 593.7 mm^2

P51 **Fri** 1. 2°C 2. 2°C 3. 2°C 4. 9 AM & 6 PM 5. 24.4°C

Brain Stretch 288 cm^2

Week 18

P52 **Mon** 1. 104.3, 96.1, 87.9 2. C 3. c/15 4. 1 5. answers will vary

Tues 1. 0.56, 0.354, 2/10 2. answers will vary 3. 67, 1 4. 27 5. 1/6

P53 **Wed** 1. trapezoid 2. 150° 3. answers will vary 4. sphere 5. answers will vary

Thurs 1. 16.5 m 2. 162.28 cm 3. 943 g 4. kL 5. 65 cm^3

P54 **Fri** 1. Friday 2. 138 3. 27 4. almost 28

Brain Stretch B

Week 19

P55 **Mon** 1. m+7 2. answers will vary 3. p=139 4. 9 5. 5, 5, 10, 15, 25, 40

Tues 1. 1.7 2. 13/20 3. < 4. 9 5. 305/13

P56 **Wed** 1. three 2. obtuse 3. answers will vary 4. 20° 5. answers will vary

Thurs 1. 26 m 2. x = 12.6 m^2 3. 490 000 mL 4. 3.55 L 5. 732 days

P57 **Fri** 1. $272.56 2. $7.89 3. $34.61 4. ARC has greatest value

Brain Stretch answers will vary

Week 20

P58 **Mon** 1. answers will vary 2. 2x – 12 = 0 3. 55 4. B 5. 11

Tues 1. $19 357.89 2. +13° 3. 0.3125 4. hundred thousand 5. 6 18/19

P59 **Wed** 1. <NTS & <STP 2. cube 3. answers will vary 4. none 5. sphere

Thurs 1. 27.7 mm 2. x = 1592.5 m^2 3. 0.3144 m 4. °C 5. 4220.2 mm^3

P60 **Fri** 1. answers will vary 2. line graph 3. 2009 4. 2005

Brain Stretch Ben is 13.5 Grandfather is 58.5

Week 21

P61 **Mon** 1. 5 2. answers will vary 3. 12 4. Multiply by 2 5. 41

Tues 1. 25 2. 1.57 3. 5^6 = 15 625 4. 3/5 5. 1/3

P62 **Wed** 1. answers will vary 2. 43° 3. one 4. 5. answers will vary

Thurs 1. 84.7m 2. 5 mL, 0.7 cL, 83 000 L 3. 486 000 g 4. 3:00 p.m. 5. 272.2 cm^2

P63 **Fri** 1. 72 combinations 2. 16 3. 40

Brain Stretch 376.8 cm

Week 22

P64 **Mon** 1. 5 2. answers will vary 3. 124 4. 7e 5. 14,27, (36), 43

Tues 1. 2883.6 2. zero point zero nine two 3. $1.46 4. -26, -4, -3, 18, 38, 45, 67 5. 1/6

P65 **Wed** 1. 59° 2. right 3. one 4. answers will vary 5. cube

Thurs answers will vary

P66 **Fri** 1. ~48 2. ¼ 3. 45/100 or 9/20 4. 46% 5. vegetables

Brain Stretch 55

Week 23

P67 **Mon** 1. 44 2. + 3. 1 4. answers will vary 5. b = a/7

Tues 1. 3.3 X 10^5 2. 385 3. 23,2,1 4. $1.40 5. 3.960

P68 **Wed** 1. none 2. 3. pyramid 4. 97° 5. right scalene triangle.

Thurs 1. 70 mm 2. existing order is correct 3. 366 days 4. 12.000 009 kg 5. 528.0 cm^3

P69 **Fri** 1. 59.5% 2. nothing He is $1 096 over budget 3. 32.6% 4. $1 440

Brain Stretch 8

Week 24

P70 **Mon** 1. -7, 19 -35 2. answers will vary 3. 25-b 4. 15.6 5. b = 4a

Tues 1. 7X2X2X2X1 2. 56 3. -35 4. $3.20 5. 2/3, 5/8, 1/4

P71 **Wed** 1. answers will vary 2. answers will vary 3. rectangular prism 4. 97° 5. rectangular prism

Thurs 1. 1:00 2. 15 cm 3. 144 months 4. 0.07 mg 5. 54.6 mm^2

P72 **Fri** 1. 31.25 s 2. 31.8 s 3. 0.8 s 4. 0.4817 min

Brain Stretch 16 cm

Week 25

P73 **Mon** 1. 40 2. answers will vary 3. 11p – 9 4. X 5. 27.5

Tues 1. 240 2. 1.669 3. 16 740 4. 18 5. 1/6

P74 **Wed** 1. trapezoid 2. acute 3. no edges 4. a 90° angle 5. right isosceles triangle

Thurs 1. 18.3 m 2. 0.007 mm; 2500 cm; 40 m 3. 144.0∏ m^2 4. 7.0341 kg 5. 294 m^3

P75 **Fri** 1. 1.2 2. 17 3. ~248 4. $744.75

Brain Stretch $2880 more

Week 26

P76 **Mon** 1. 128 2. answers will vary 3. + 4. 8(r-45) 5. C

Tues 1. 13.78 2. 5.9, 2.80, 2.5, 0.718. 0.02 3. $2^4 = 16$ 4. 210 5. 250.0

P77 **Wed** 1. 44° 2. answers will vary 3. tetrahedron 4. answers will vary 5. none

Thurs 1. 155 cm^2 2. 5.122 L 3. 1:15 p.m. 4. hours 5. 789.3 mg

P78 **Fri** 1. C 2. D 3. 70% 4. 0.777 5. none

Brain Stretch 5357 m

Week 27

P79 **Mon** 1. answers will vary 2. 3(g+41) 3. 800 000 000 4. 6 5. 84, 124, 199, 228

Tues 1. 0.3000 2. 5X3X2X1 3. $6^3 = 216$ 4. 22.5 5. 132

P80 **Wed** 1. two 2. see drawing 3. see drawing 4. 70° 5. acute

Thurs 1. 23 m 2. 268 weeks 3. 12.5∏ mm^2 4. 8 mm; 0.04 m; 2,900 cm 5. h=14; V=1356

P81 **Fri** (a)8 hrs (b) 2 hrs (c) 8 hrs (d) 1 hr (e)1 hr (f) 1 hrs (g) 2 hrs (h) 1 hr

1. A, C 2. 3 hrs 3. D, E, F, H received one hour, E, N, G received 2 hours, B, G, A, C received 8 hours 4. Internet, phone/texting, sports practice, exercising

Brain Stretch 1.89%

Week 28

P82 **Mon** 1. 27 2. X 3. 43/o 4. 10 5. B

Tues 1. 100.88 2. 310.0 3. < 4. 4.53109 5. +$500

P83 **Wed** 1. 60° 2. two 3. No (Angles are not 90°) 4. answers will vary 5. answers will vary

Thurs 1. mm 2. 15 mm 3. 365 000 4. 3040 mg 5. 9hrs and 8 mins

P84 **Fri** 1. 0.78 2. ~58 3. 6 fewer families 4. 0.95

Brain Stretch $130 was the cost and no she did not get change because she did not have enough $

Week 29

P85 **Mon** 1. answers will vary 2. 9a - 6=30 3. $2k^2 + 4k - 2$ 4. 2048 5. b = a /5

Tues 1. -72 2. 5×10^4 3. -$452. 4. 1/2, 3/4, 5/6 5. 63

P86 **Wed** 1. answers will vary 2. right 3. pyramid 4. angle measuring more than 90°, but less than 180° 5. square

Thurs 1. 81.0∏ mm^2 2. 861 000 g 3. 8:30 p.m. 4. seconds or minutes 5. h=10; surface area = 460

P87 **Fri** 1. triple bar graph 2. Grade 7 (29.5) 3. 0.80 4. 86 students

Brain Stretch 6 cups milk, 9 cups flour, 5 1/3 cups other

Week 30

P88 **Mon** 1. $11g^4 + 2g$ 2. answers will vary 3. ÷ 4. 8 5. 20

Tues 1. 4/5, 0.8000 2. =34 3. 5,5,3,1 4. 112/17 5. 360

P89 **Wed** 1. rhombus 2. answers will vary 3. answers will vary 4. answers will vary 5. semi-chord

Thurs 1. 5 m 2. seconds 3. 10:45 p.m. 4. 0.3 cm; 350 mm; 80 m 5. c=22.8

P90 **Fri** answers will vary

Brain Stretch Not quite, it would take 2.56 hrs.